FRANCE

OMPIÈGNE • Soissons

NTILLY

E

REIMS

• Douaumont
Verdun

Metz

L O R R A I N E

RIE

Provins

UX·LE VICOMTE

NANCY

Domrémy

U

Troyes

VITTEL

Sens

C H A M P A G N E

Bourbonne
les Bains

sur-Loire

TANLAY

FONTAINE FRANÇAISE

VEZELAY

• DIJON

B O U R G O G N E

BESANÇON

la Charite

• Nevers

Autun

LEGEND

Cathedral

Chateau

URBONNAIS

Moulins

Tournus

THE HALO ON THE SWORD

The Halo
ON THE SWORD
ST. JOAN OF ARC

by MARY PURCELL

With a Preface by
CLAUDE FARRÈRE
Member of the French Academy

THE NEWMAN PRESS
Westminster, Maryland
1952

Nihil Obstat:
  EDUARDUS GALLEN,
    Censor Theol. Deput.

Imprimi Potest:
  ✠ IOANNES CAROLUS,
    Archiep. Dublinen.,
      Hiberniae Primas.
DUBLINI, *die 16° Novembris, anno* 1951.

Library of Congress Catalog Card Number: 52–10386

For
My Father and Mother

Preface

HERE IS a book which is strangely new.
It is certainly not the first time that an English-speaking writer has undertaken the story of Jeanne d'Arc. Shakespeare was the first to decide to treat the vast subject of the virgin of Domrémy. But he made of it merely an addition to his *Henry VI*, and his portrait is nothing but a caricature. Dare I even say what I really think? I do not believe that the exaggerated rhapsodies of *Henry V, Henry VI, Titus Andronicus* and even *Timon of Athens* are from the pen of the author of *Othello*, of *Hamlet* and of *King Lear*. Black and white are less unlike. In any case, Jeanne d'Arc, written by the author of *Henry VI*, whoever he may have been, is not worth reading. And I would say as much of almost everything that the English have written of this wonderful maiden, who once drove them out of France—including therein the admittedly picturesque play of Bernard Shaw. It seems as if the subject itself were somewhat disconcerting to the Anglo-Saxons.

Yet many of them approached it with the greatest respect, and even with an obvious desire to render full justice to the martyr of Rouen—anxious also to erase the muddy stain which the torture of Jeanne had left on the honour of England. Although it must be remembered that the English were not the only executioners of the Maid; the Burgundians had a large share in the crime and many Frenchmen, too—at their head the "gentil" and ungrateful Dauphin, whom she herself had consecrated King. He could have saved Jeanne; he refrained out of cowardice and caution. No matter! That the martyrdom of the Maid greatly served the cause of King Charles VII, and was detrimental to that of his enemies—of the unhappy Henry VI, in particular—there is today no doubt. But that England was more or less dishonoured by it, that no longer is beyond question. And that is evidently the reason why so many honest Englishmen have done their best to mitigate this dishonour in pleading guilty, in advancing at the same time in defence the extenuating circumstances of those bygone days, with their different customs, and of an exaggerated and misdirected patriotism.

Not one of them has succeeded. And the real story of Jeanne d'Arc, seen from a British standpoint, but judged impartially, without paradox or plea, still remains to be written.

Why?

Numerous reasons might be given, but, in my opinion, they might all be résuméed in one:

The Anglo-Saxons are Protestants. And Jeanne d'Arc was a Catholic. That is to say, she belonged to a race which the Anglo-Saxons, as Protestants, cannot understand.

They are not alone in that. Modern France, steeped in a materialism which is killing her, is no longer capable of understanding anything of the mystery of Jeanne d'Arc. And to say nothing of the stupid anti-clericals, followers of Voltaire, nor of the mediocre intellects, such as Anatole France, even sincere men, like Michelet, failed to hear the Voices which prompted the shepherdess of Domrémy along the way of her Calvary. Only genuine Catholics can penetrate the depths of that dazzling and simple soul which was the soul of the Maid of Orleans.

And that is why Miss Mary Purcell's book has every chance of being a success after so many understandable failures—failures which could be nothing else but failures.

For Mary Purcell, an Irishwoman, is a Catholic. And I did not need to read ten pages of her book to realise that her belief is sincere. That she has faith, simple and implicit faith. Miss Purcell does not merely believe, like so many half-hearted Christians, in God, in Jesus Christ His only Son, Our Lord, Who was conceived by the Holy Ghost and born of the Virgin Mary. She believes in many other things. And, notably, in Jeanne d'Arc and in her Voices. If you do not believe in them yourself, you will never be able to conceive how a humble shepherdess succeeded in accomplishing such a series of extraordinary feats: in crossing France in a state of war, from the depths of Lorraine to the Castle of Chinon; in persuading "le gentil Dauphin"—timorous, troubled, doubtful of his legitimacy, doubtful, consequently, of his right to the throne, that he was, on the contrary, the true Son of

France and the sole legitimate heir of those twenty kings, his ancestors; in reconciling the different proud, jealous and lethargic lords; in inspiring the hordes of old troopers, who had never fought but for themselves and for gain and plunder; in opposing them to disciplined, well-trained English troops; in leading them to victory, often against the judgment of their chiefs; in liberating Orleans; then in marching from Orleans to Rheims, bringing with her the Dauphin, frightened and hesitating, and there consecrating him King—King by the Will of God.

And you will understand even less how Jeanne d'Arc, her task accomplished, tempted to exceed her mission, met with reverses, treachery, and finally fell into the hands of her enemies, so that her achievements might, as it were, be sealed with her very blood and that her martyrdom might prove her sanctity and re-awaken in the kingdom of France that patriotism that had lain dormant since the death of the saintly King Louis IX.

.   .   .   .   .

Mary Purcell has understood all the miracles of the Maid of Orleans, for the all-powerful reason that she herself believes in miracles, being a Catholic, Apostolic and Roman; and believes in the Holy Ghost, Who conceived Jesus in the womb of a Virgin; and believes in the Holy Church, built on a rock chosen by Jesus; and believes in the Communion of the Saints who spoke to the shepherdess Jeanne "in better words than yours"—or mine—and believes in the forgiveness of sins, the resurrection of the body; in short, in all that materialism proclaims absurd and impossible. "Credo quia absurdum impossibilique," replies the Catholic; for which reason alone he is incapable of misinterpretation where Jeanne d'Arc is concerned.

. . . . .

And finally, here is the only book written about Jeanne d'Arc in the English tongue which is likely not to be unreasonable—which even has a definite chance of surpassing most of the French books dealing with the same subject.

France today, turned away from Christianity—in depth, if not in extent—has succeeded only in producing works as dull as those of Anatole France, or as unnecessarily lyrical as that of Michelet. Between ourselves, I believe, in all sincerity, that Ireland, where the Catholic Faith, strengthened by persecution, has maintained its fervour, is the only country capable of supplying an author worthy of handling, without sacrilege or sentimentality, the supernatural and superhuman mystery which is the history of the Maid of Orleans.

. . . . .

Here then is the book.

Far be it from me to judge it. I am incapable of doing so, firstly, because, though conversant with Shakespeare, Kipling and Morgan, I do not read English easily; secondly, because my Catholic Faith, although fervent, has not the youthfulness—dare I say the violence?—of that of Mary Purcell. I leave it to the Irish to criticise this book which I trust will be quickly translated into French. Our translators are justly said to be the best in the world. The incomparable Tabalet, Hérelle and Robert d'Humières are, alas, already dead, but they have left us their successors in the persons of Jackson, Varlet, Vallette and

that amazing woman, Henriette Doringe. It is up to them
to give us without delay a French translation of Mary
Purcell, and for a French publisher to edit the only book
which gives, in accuracy and quiet enthusiasm, a worthy
picture of "la bonne Lorraine qu'Anglais brûlèrent à
Rouen."

CLAUDE FARRÈRE,
May, 1951.

Chapter One

ALTHOUGH THE Duke of Burgundy was a traitor, Providence permitted him to prosper. It was strange, agreed the little girl, wondering what a traitor might be; she thought it odd that the old man should say Providence when his glance towards Heaven had shown that he meant the good God; shading her eyes from the September sun to follow old Perrin's gaze, she decided that to prosper was to own many glossy-coated horses and gaily-painted, heavily-laden wagons such as those now approaching them, making splashes of colour all the way down the hill from Bermont to Greux.

Taking hold of the gnarled old hand stretched out to her, she hoisted herself to an excellent vantage-point on a grassy bank and waited impatiently for the Burgundian wagon-train to reach where she and Papa Perrin sat. It was so fascinating to watch the tossing manes of the big horses and the gaudy wagons bulging with bales of merchandise—all very wonderful in a world where wagons,

1

as often as not, went unpainted, and where loads were drawn at snail's pace by dull, weary-eyed oxen.

Only a week previously the same twelve-horse wagons, with their blue-capped carters, had trundled by, bearing the great wine-casks to far Flanders, some ninety leagues to the north. This time they were returning, rumbling and creaking along the old Roman road that ran by the marches of Lorraine; the Langres road some called it— others the Burgundy road. On distant slopes the beech-trees, burnished to ruddy gold, glowed against a back-ground of sombre firs; near to where the child and the old man sat, the oaks of the Bois Chenu lifted grateful arms to the light; and in the valley, Domrémy and Maxey and other little hamlets studded the Meuse as it shimmered in the mellow sunlight, like beads on a rosary. The wagoners flicked lightly at the flies that buzzed about the horses' heads; that was the worst of a road running by a river, they grumbled, the flies never gave oneself or one's team a moment's peace.

"Where are they coming from now, Papa Perrin?" asked the child, as the foremost wagon appeared round the bend of the road.

"From some Flemish city; from Ghent or Antwerp perhaps, or Ypres or Delft; or maybe from Bruges."

"Bruges! Where the beautiful bells you told me about chime so often? Oh, Papa Perrin, I wish one of yon wagoners were my father. He might bring me to Bruges."

"So! Old Perrin's bell-ringing isn't good enough for you any more. There's my thanks for never failing to ring the *Ave Maria* since the day you scolded me for forgetting. And you'd rather have one of John of Burgundy's blue-caps for your father than honest Jacques d'Arc. You're a nice one, you are."

But the bells of Bruges were forgotten now that the first wagon had drawn abreast. So full of awe was the little one that her voice sank to a whisper.

"I can see the whites of the horses' eyes; that's a sign a horse is vicious, isn't it, Papa Perrin?" Then, without waiting for an answer, "A scarlet wagon! I wonder what's in those bales?"

"Oh, silks and velvets for the grand ladies of Dijon, no doubt; and fine red leather for their slippers; and ribbons and laces and sparkling jewels."

"Here's a blue wagon. Is there anything for the fine ladies in this one? And, Papa Perrin, who's the woman sitting in between the bales?"

"That's the *béguine*, the woman who looks after the kitchens and the storerooms for the Duchess. Every great lady has a *béguine* to look after things; she has been to the shops in the big towns in the Lowlands buying whatever her mistress ordered."

"What sort of things?"

"How should I know? Gorgeous clothes and furs for their winter robes; and some of that high headgear they wear, with horns as long as those of the stag in the Bois Chenu."

"What the wandering friar was angry about the day he preached on the bridge yonder?"

"Yes, indeed; the very same. Poor man, he might have saved his breath, talking to us plain folk about such fripperies. I suppose he couldn't get them 'twas meant for to listen to him; and even if they heard him they'd hardly pay much heed. How well your little ears took in what he said!"

"You haven't guessed what's in the last two that passed. What's in this one now?"

"God knows. I'm sure I don't. More fine feathers to deck the fine birds of courtiers, I suppose; and fal-lals to pass their time."

"I hear something jingling, Papa Perrin. Is it the fal-lals?"

"The cap-and-bells for the Duke's jester, maybe; or some such baubles for all the fools and idlers that hang about great folk's houses."

The wagons—saffron, mauve, cream and Burgundy-blue—succeeded one another, each wagoner allowing a generous space between his wagon and the one just before, for the dust-clouds to settle. On the second wagon the steward of the Duke's household and the *béguine* employed by the Duchess were comfortably ensconced between the bales. The steward was keeping a wary eye on the road ahead, fearing an attack by one of the many outlaw bands that infested the countryside. He reminded the *béguine* of the time, not so very long gone, when just such a wagon-train had been ambushed about six miles from this very spot; the wretches had ripped open the bales with daggers and knives; never would the steward forget the sight of those ruffians trampling the priceless tapestries of Arras in the mire and wrapping the loot in the rich brocades intended for Church vestments.

Yes, the *béguine* remembered, and piously hoped that nothing of the sort would happen this trip when all the court ladies were waiting on her return with the cambric for their shifts and the cashmere for their *blanchets*. She mused over the trouble she had taken in choosing the satiny damasks for their boudoirs; and smiled to herself thinking of how pleased the Duchess would be with the snowy linen for the serving-maids' wimples, with the flagons of crystal to grace her tables and the tinkling glass chandeliers to hang in her great halls.

The steward's mind had also begun to check-up on the contents of each wagon; there was the court apothecary's order—perfumes and unguents and balsams; the order for the Duchess—inlaid tables and cabinets, convex mirrors and silver candlesticks; chessmen cunningly carved in ebony and ivory; the new-fangled hand-painted playing cards, with Charlemagne for King of Hearts and other famous Frenchmen and women, some living, some long dead, depicted on the other court cards. And for the Duke there were pewter tankards and gilded goblets; armour and lances for himself and his knights; vellum for his monks and scriveners; marbles and fragrant incense for his churches; tapestries for the walls and glass for the mullioned windows of his palaces at Dijon and Rouvres.

From his perch on one of the mountains of merchandise that lumbered and swayed on the Langres road, a minstrel nudged the showman who was his travelling companion, and, with nervous gestures, indicated on the one side the pine and beech-clad slopes of Bar, meet hiding-places for some robber captain and his rascally band, and on the other some fortress or castle of Lorraine, from whence at any moment the Orleanists—

Armagnacs they were calling them now—might make a sudden swoop on the Duke's retainers.

"I begin to regret the day I agreed to travel to the court of Dijon." The minstrel spoke more to himself than to the other.

"People say that it's the grandest castle and the gayest court in Christendom," said the showman, fondling a monkey, his stock-in-trade.

But the minstrel was not reassured. With one hand he straightened the blue Burgundian cap on his poll, while with the other he made sure that the white scarf of Orleans was still in his satchel; on the road to Dijon it was as well to travel prepared for all emergencies, and he had been warned in Flanders that, in these parts, a change of colour was often more useful than a change of linen. The showman's monkey startled him by suddenly jumping up and down and gesticulating madly, but it was only a little girl and an old man who were sitting on a bank nearby that had excited the creature. The showman quieted him and held him up to practise making a courtly bow and doffing his tiny blue cap with a sweeping gesture—a trick that he would have to do often in Dijon, but which was, his master thought, probably wasted on yonder old peasant and his grandchild.

"Papa Perrin! What's that funny thing waving the little blue cap at us? Is that the Duke's jester? Where's the bells?"

"No, no. That's not the jester; the jester's a Christian same as all of us. Yon thing's a monkey, a hairy little beast from foreign lands; showmen keep them and teach them tricks to make folks laugh. Last year it was a man with a bear that went to Dijon for the winter; the bear got away just beyond Greux and everyone had a rare time chasing him in the woods. Another time there was a tumbler who did his cartwheels on the bridge yonder; all the lads spent weeks afterwards trying to do the same."

Jeannette sighed. It would have been fun if that monkey had made off for the Bois Chenu; what a chase the children would give him! As if the Duke of Burgundy had not enough of good things in all those wagons . . . God was certainly being very kind to him letting him have a monkey, too. What was it that the friar had said . . . "to prosper"; yes, God had allowed the wicked to prosper. . . . The Great Duke must be shockingly bad to be allowed to prosper so.

"Papa Perrin! What bad things did Duke John do?"

"Well, for one thing, he had our good Duke Louis of Orleans—his own cousin, mark you—murdered."

"Why?"

"You are too small to understand. Our poor King Charles was mad—he's that still, poor gentleman, and more's the pity, for they say he would have been a good King for France—and the two Dukes were at loggerheads as to who should rule in the name of the King, so Duke John just hired a gang of assassins who set about my Lord of Orleans in the streets of Paris one evening and hacked him to pieces."

"When did they do that?"

"Long before you were born. Almost twelve years ago."

"And was Duke John punished for murdering his cousin?"

"Not he. Burgundy's much too cunning for that. He got word that his Paris lodging was going to be searched and his men-at-arms questioned closely; so he fled to Flanders, his country in the north, and stayed there until the hubbub had died down; then he begged pardon of the young orphaned Orleans children—with his tongue in his cheek, of course; and ever since, he has taken the side of the English against Orleans and France. Oh, he's a low traitor, is Burgundy; a man of blood. I wouldn't have his conscience for all that's in those wagons. It's a terrible thing for a Frenchman to be the means of shedding so much French blood."

Jeannette agreed again, her solemn eyes on the last wagon of all; she wondered why the showman with the monkey had not been allowed to ride in this one; he had been almost slithering off the one he shared with the lutist. This wagon seemed to be empty; as it came nearer she saw in its shadowed interior two brown-garbed figures. The old man beside her was dragging himself stiffly to his feet; he touched Jeannette's shoulder, indicating the two in the wagon. "Poor Clare nuns," he said, and began hobbling towards the roadway. "Maybe it's the holy one from Corbie, the Blessed Colette."

.   .   .   .   .

The nun who had been known in the world as Agnes de Vaux sighed as the cart jolted herself and her companion almost off the board that served them for a seat. What a journey it had been! The last five weeks had been a nightmare, with its endless hours in this wagon and the constant travelling. A useless trip, too, chasing their benefactor, John of Burgundy, first through the

Flemish cities, then from one French town to another, always on his heels but never catching up with him, until finally in Troyes they had been told that he had ridden west to Montereau to hold parley with the Dauphin. It was only then that *la Mère*—as the nuns affectionately called their Abbess, Dame Colette—decided to give up trying to get in touch with him. One would imagine that *la Mère* should have been glad to hear that Duke John had gone to meet his foe in peace, not in war; but it was not so. On hearing this news, she had murmured to herself: "Montereau! Too late! Too late!" And after some time spent in prayer she had begged the good people of Troyes to give the two Poor Clares speedy transport to Neufchâtel, where they would meet the Burgundian wagon-train on its return journey to Flanders. It would be a relief, thought her companion nun, to get back to the quiet Abbey of Auxonne, or maybe *la Mère* would go to Besançon first; any place would be Heaven after the noisy cities and towns, the weary hours sitting in the wagon where those brutes of horses jolted one so. But *la Mère*, sensing her thoughts, said:

"Neither to Auxonne nor Besançon; to the palace at Dijon. The Duchess helped us in our beginnings and got her lord to give our nuns the Abbeys where we can be apart from the world for our work of intercession and reparation. She will be in need of comfort tonight; we go to her." Then she began to pray earnestly for the Duke, saying the prayers for those about to die, every now and then pausing for a while before starting off afresh with "let us pray for Duke John." Each time she repeated his name, the other nun was reminded of the time when Jean sans Peur had stamped into their quiet enclosure, his armour clanging about his short, thickset body, his enormous head thrust forward, his face glowering to left and right—the only sign of softness in him being his regard for *la Mère*. "Pray for me, Lady Abbess. Pray for me," he would say when Dame Colette thanked him for his gifts to the Order. Ah, dear; they were not only praying for him now, they were suffering sore with the stuffiness and the jolting of his wagon. Ah! for the ox-wagons of poorer patrons . . . "Let us pray for Duke John . . ."

Meanwhile, the musician and the showman were discussing the prospects before them in the ducal court. They hoped that there might be some slight respite from the wars in which the Great Duke seemed to be constantly embroiled—for the period of their engagement in Dijon at least. When he was not fighting for or against the Paris mob, he was giving battle to the Armagnacs, or to one of the free-booters—sometimes, indeed, making common cause with the latter; and his alliance with the English invaders meant ceaseless war against the rest of France, if it could be said that there was much of France left when one discounted the English and Burgundian possessions. But something was afoot yonder! The wagoner was whipping up his team to shorten the gap between his wagon and the preceding one. The musician stared ahead, apprehension in every line of his face.

"What goes on?" he quavered.

"That I don't know—yet. Hoi!" he called to his comrade, who was in a better position to know, "what's happening?"

"The young lads fighting again, I think," shouted back

the other. "Let's halt and look on; the steward is getting down himself; my legs need stretching and your monkey-man is perilously near breaking his neck the way he's leaning over the side of your load there."

"Hey, you!" the carter glanced over his shoulder at his second passenger. "What's wrong?"

"It's my monkey. The shouting frightened him and he's climbing down among these bales somewhere."

"We're halting now for a little while and you can get him. Come on," he called to the minstrel, "there will be fun on the bridge; the lads of Domrémy and Maxey have fights there; the Domrémy folk are King's men and the Maxey boys good Burgundians."

On the road beyond the bridge a miniature battle was in progress; about twenty boys were engaged, some in close combat, where they flailed one another with fists and bare feet; some at a safer distance were throwing stones. The wagoners leaned on the parapet of the bridge to watch and to cheer the Maxey lads; the monkey chattered madly to his master and danced up and down; the musician, glad to be off his uncomfortable perch for a few minutes, walked about limbering his legs and lightly touching a note here and there on his lute, wondering what would suit his mixed audience. How funny that old man looked as he trotted along doffing his cap to the taller of the two nuns! "My God! Blessed Colette!" he ejaculated, recognising her.

She seemed to draw the people towards her; the peasants came flocking from their doorways, where they—the loyalist inhabitants of the twin border-villages of Domrémy and Greux—had been watching, with dour eyes, the passing of the wagon-train that spoke so loudly of the wealth and power of Burgundy; now they came to Colette, asking for prayers, kissing the hem of her rough habit, murmuring to one another how good it was when she passed their way—she who brought happiness and left blessings. The showman could be heard telling the lutist that she was the only woman who might travel in safety through war-torn France in these bad times; not an Armagnac nor Burgundian, not the worst brigand in the realm, not even an English *Goddam*, would lay a finger on her who was so near and dear to the good God.

The Abbess turned to the minstrel and bade him make music. He hesitated a moment, wondering what to play; then he noticed the little girl who had trailed along behind the nuns; she reminded him of his own little Marie, now long dead; he would play the old hymn to the Blessed Mother that everyone in France, whether Burgundian or Armagnac, knew from childhood. He began softly, diffidently, being somewhat shy of the wagoners; but he need not have minded; soon many voices joined in, clear, robust tenors and throaty baritones: *O Holy Mary, Mother of the Lord;* the clamour of the children ceased; stones fell from burning fists, and hands, ready to strike, unclenched themselves; *into thy hands and His;* the boys, grinning at recent enemies, turned with one accord across the bridge; *with certain hope I commit myself;* the little girl was standing apart from the group smiling, but not joining in the singing; *O Lady, defence of all who seek thy aid. Holy Mary, Mother of God, pray for us sinners now and at the hour of our death. Amen.*

A silence ensued. The loyalists and the Duke's retainers had united in singing to their mutual Mother; it would savour of desecration to relapse into animosity just now; old Perrin, who was not unknown to some of the Burgundy men—they having often stopped for Mass in either Domrémy or Greux, in both of which churches he served as bell-ringer—asked questions about their journeyings since last they had passed; the steward, always mindful of the account he would have to give of his purchases, and anxious to be in the good graces of these Armagnacs through whose territory he hoped to pass safely, adopted a genial tone as he replied; the showman put his monkey through his paces, to the delight of the children and some of the grown-ups.

A little way from the crowd, whither she had withdrawn when the musician had started the hymn, *la Mère* was moving towards a little girl who stared; her companion was slightly shocked when Colette knelt in the dust beside the little one, threw her arms around her and kissed her on the forehead; *la Mère* had a habit of doing the most extraordinary things, but to remain steadfastly gazing into the eyes of this sturdy, rather stolid-looking little daughter of the fields was surely not the thing for a Poor Clare. In public, too.

"What is your name, *mignonne?*"

"Jeannette, madame, Jeannette."

"Jeannette," whispered *la Mère*, "Daughter of God. Daughter of God." The other nun was getting uneasy; the wagoners were cracking their whips; one was heard to say that he would wait no longer even if he *did* drive a saint; the ex-belligerents were fidgeting. "Oh, dear!"

thought the Poor Clare with a fresh access of distress, "what if she goes into an ecstasy? She looks just like she did that day on the road to Moulins, when the crowds ran to see and touch her. Dear God, not here, not here, I beg You. . . ."

Sounds of furious galloping came from the south; the steward shaded his eyes and stared at the coming caval-cade; lances glittered in the late sunlight. "Knights of Burgundy," someone said. The Domrémy folk drew apart, ready to run towards the woods should need arise.

"Something forgotten again, I'll wager," said the steward. "If so, the pack-horses or the mules may go back, with some knights for escort. I won't send one of those teams to do that journey again. Horses and men can't be kept on the road forever." The wagoners nodded approval. *La Mère* was praying aloud, no one listening to her but the One to Whom she was speaking. The horsemen flung themselves from their mounts and rushed to her, breathless.

"We were sent to fetch you. There is great trouble in Dijon."

"I know, my son. Duke John was killed at Montereau today."

A hush that was half-horror at the news, half-amaze-ment at the visionary's knowledge, fell upon the crowd.

"Let us go to console her." Mère Colette spoke to her companion and turned towards the wagon.

"Her Grace's carriage follows; it should be but half-a-league behind," said a knight, preparing to re-mount.

The wagoners, stunned and silent, went each man to

his team. The lutist and showman moved towards one another, impelled by common cause.

"Monkeys won't be needed in Dijon this winter."

"No. Nor music. How think you shall we get back again through this war-ridden land? I knew I should never have come."

"Cheer up. There are other great lords. Let's keep together and give shows along the road. We'll be Orleanists here in Domrémy; Burgundians further on; brigands if we meet the Grand Companies; and *Goddams* as good as any of the Englishmen if we come across them."

They moved towards Domrémy church; the boys had again split into separate groups and were glaring at one another, remembering their wounds; their elders excitedly discussed the news.

"Just the time to begin," said the showman, nudging the musician who began playing a gay air; the monkey capered and gestured and searched for his cap which his master had confiscated and hidden. All the children laughed again and drew near to see; all but one; she stood back in the shadows watching the last wagon vanish into the dusk. Fragments of conversation floated on the air.

"Got his deserts, I say."

"Two wrongs don't make a right, Pierre."

"The Dauphin's men. Some of the knights said that the Dauphin himself was there," muttered d'Epinal, the only Burgundian sympathiser in Domrémy.

Jeannette turned homewards; it was cool in their garden; it would be quiet there; mignonette grew by the path; that was what the saint had called her—

mignonne—she remembered as the scent of the little plant rose to greet her. At the end of their garden was the church; thither she walked slowly, repeating to herself *"Mignonne . . . mignonne . . . mignonne."* But there was another name the saint had said. A more wonderful name. As she recalled it, her little brown hands lifted and joined almost of themselves; she went down on her knees on the sanded path where it ended at the church; pressing her brow against the grey wall she spoke her happiness to the stone. "Daughter of God," she said exultingly, repeating the words slowly to herself and to the rough wall, "Daughter of God . . ." Then, raising her face to the skies, where already one star was shining, she called softly into the vault of Heaven: "Father! . . . Father! . . . Father!"

Chapter Two

THE THREE sons of Jacques d'Arc fidgeted and squirmed uneasily and stole shamefaced looks—now at their father, now at their mother, now at one another. Their mother bent over the *potage* as if her very life depended on its stirring; whenever she desisted for a moment, Jacques would resume speaking with vehement haste. His wife shook her head as she stirred; he was a good husband and father, but he had his share of faults; up to the time that their daughter Catherine died last year, he had hardly noticed Jeanne. Till then he had called her Jeannette, not seeming to realise what a misfit the baby-name—long discarded by everyone else—was for the tall, lissom girl. Now, like most men with one daughter, he made himself silly in his solicitude for the girl. If she were a giddy maid, fond of dancing and merrymaking, there might be some cause for concern, but—Jeanne! Even the priest had said that her like was not to be found in the three parishes. The trouble with

Jeanne was to get her to go to any little local festivities; these last years she had been too much inclined to go off alone—no way to attract a husband, her mother told her, to get spoken of as being a little peculiar; if one wanted solitude there were cloisters where those so minded could give themselves up to that way of life, if sure they were called to it. But Jeanne had only smiled; she *was* a good child, thought her mother, even though she had some odd ways; when she grew out of these difficult years of girlhood this silly hankering after solitude would pass, and as the girl was strong, hard-working and healthy—qualities most necessary for a peasant-farmer's wife—she would attract some good husband in time. Michael Lebuin, now. . . But, dear! dear! There was Jacques ranting away, making mountains out of molehills as usual—hark at the man!

"It is because this is Saturday and she will have gone to visit the shrine at Bermont that I have called you all to listen to me. Jeanne had better not know. And one word of what I say is not to go beyond this house. Do you hear?" His voice rasped as it rose.

"Keep calm, Jacques. Why on earth do you excite yourself so?"

"I had a dream about our Jeanne, Isabel. Such a dream! It was so real. But so foul and awful——"

"Something you ate; or, more likely, something you drank. You're too fond of going round to help the neighbours at vintage-time and for long afterwards; you help yourself to too much new wine and then complain about dreams."

"Wine or no wine, this dream took such a hold on me——"

"Don't you know that it is forbidden to believe in dreams?"

"I know, Isabel, I know; but as this particular dream was about Jeanne and the dreadful fate that overtook her, I had to tell you and the boys about it."

"Well, tell us at once, or she'll be back."

"I dreamt that I saw her—I saw her riding with soldiers."

"Jacquot d'Arc!" It was a sure sign that Isabel was perturbed to the uttermost when she called her husband "Jacquot." "To even repeat the like about your own daughter—as good a girl as is in all Lorraine, and you know it, even though it is her own mother who says so. Before the boys, too!" The good woman glared at her spouse.

"The boys have to hear such things sometime; better from me than from some worse quarter. Pierre! Jacquemin! Jean! Attend to me. You remember when we had to fly to Neufchâteau last year—the time the Burgundians raided Domrémy and Greux; when we stayed in the house of the woman they called *la Rousse?*"

"Yes, father." The boys' eyes studied the earthen floor intently.

"I warned you about the droves of women and girls that we saw following the Duke's army; indeed, they follow every army in these times; some soldiers won't set out for the wars unless sure of a supply of such women——"

"Jacques!" Isabel's reproach rang to the rafters.

"It's true, *maman*, and well you know it; isn't that what became of that girl from Saint-Germain? I warned our boys at that time that no decent girls rode out with soldiers—no matter what army the soldiers serve. But I dreamt that I saw her—our Jeanne—riding to the wars." He paused to wrestle with the emotion that threatened to overcome him. "I saw her, on a charger, in the midst of many squires and men-at-arms, with not a woman in the company."

His hearers stared at him, aghast at the implications suggested.

He choked for a moment, then collected himself again. "I brought you here to tell you that if ever the like should happen—which the good God forbid!—I would strangle her first with these two hands sooner than let her go with them. And you, boys, promise me that if such a fate should befall your sister, and that I were not here to prevent it, you must kill her. Promise me."

"Kill Jeanne!" Pierre was the only one to speak.

"Yes; it would be better for the honour of this family—humble and poor people though we are—that you would tie your sister in a sack weighted with stones and drown her in the mill-pond yonder."

"Drown who in the mill-pond?" asked the tall girl who came in on her father's last words.

"Oh, Jeanne! You startled me, coming in so quickly." Her mother hastened to reply, giving Jacques time to recover himself. "Your father thinks that stray cat has some disease and that she had better be drowned before some of the other animals take it from her."

Jeanne d'Arc looked round at her family; it was seldom that all were here together in the afternoon as they were now. The boys looked uncomfortable, they must have been catching it from Father for something; he had heard that they were fighting with the Maxey boys again, probably; she looked from them to her father and mother, then suddenly braced herself to tell them something she had been intending to tell them this long while back.

"Father! Mother!" She tossed back her straight black hair and spoke fast, urgently: "I want to go away. I want to ride with the Dauphin's men. I want to go to France."

"Oh, God! It's my dream," Jacques d'Arc groaned aloud; her brothers stared at her, horror in their eyes; Isabel rose from her stool on the hearthstone and approached her daughter, saying: "My Jeanne, you don't know what you speak about."

Jacques d'Arc, deciding that swift action was the best in such a situation, looked Jeanne straight in the face. "I was just saying, before you came in, that if ever I heard of you riding with troopers I would kill you with my own two hands. See!" And he stretched out two horny hands that he could scarcely see for tears. "And I have your brothers' promise that if I were not here—sooner than let you take up so shameful a life—they must put you in a sack and drown you in the mill-pond. And every word of that I mean; dear as you are to me, that's what I'll have done to you if you go riding after an army; so help me, God!" And, brushing past the girl, he flung out of the house.

The three boys stood up and shuffled out in shame-faced silence. The mother bit her lip, wondering what she ought to say to Jeanne, standing so erect against the wall. Better get it over—now.

"Jeanne. Your father had a dream; he dreamt he saw you riding away with troopers. As I told you last year in Neufchâteau, only loose-living women do the like. Why on earth do you want to ride with the Dauphin's men? Is it some soldier—God knows we see enough of them passing the roads these times—is it one of them who has been coaxing you to go with him to the wars?"

"Oh, no!"

"Then what on earth puts such a wild notion into your head? I think we had better arrange a marriage for you, my girl. Michael Lebuin, now——"

"No, mother. Michael has spoken to me, himself; he knows that I will not think of marrying for a few years yet."

"Not think of marrying yet! In a few years' time Michael may not think of marrying *you*. That's a foolish way to go on, putting on airs and graces with an eligible lad; you'll be getting yourself talked of as an oddity. I have no patience with such silly talk—and then that outlandish idea of riding to the wars; no wonder your father was furious——"

"Maids could ride to battle and still be as good as——"

"Will you talk sense, girl! How could anyone live among troopers and keep virtuous? Even if one wanted to preserve modesty and purity, how could it be done, living in the midst of an army—dressing, washing oneself, sleeping amidst men? I hadn't meant to speak like this, but you don't seem to realise what it means to ride to wars. You might go with the best of intentions, and find out the dangers too late. Let me hear no more of it now." (How pale the girl had gone; perhaps it was some little passing mental stress that accounted for these queer notions; so many girls of that age got a bit peculiar; it might be a good idea to send her on another visit to "Uncle" Laxart in Burey-le-Petit.)

Slowly the girl took the hoe from the corner where her father had thrown it and went out to weed the garden. Her mother's eyes followed her. Isabel Romée, clucking with annoyance to herself, wondered what would happen now if Michael Lebuin took Jeanne at her word and looked elsewhere for a wife for himself. She was a devout woman, this swarthy-faced wife of Jacques d'Arc; the only woman in the Meuse valley who had made the arduous pilgrimage to Our Lady of Puy; the only one to venture as far west as Our Lady of Chartres; her faith, devotion and strength of purpose were well-known and well-tried; illiterate, as were so many of her neighbours, she was, nevertheless, an intelligent and well-informed woman. News of happenings throughout France and, indeed, throughout Christendom, filtered into this quiet countryside in a steady trickle; there were the soldiers going to and returning from the wars; there were the travelling friars and nuns; the merchants, pedlars and showmen, who were constantly to be seen on the high-road that ran through Domrémy. Many a one, pausing to pray in the little church, was glad to accept Isabel's invitation to rest awhile in her garden; on winter nights, travellers, caught unawares in a storm, were bidden welcome to such poor hospitality as Jacques d'Arc and his wife had to offer—a bed of clean straw beside the hearth, a bowl of steaming soup, a hunk of rye-bread.

Isabel smiled to herself at the very idea of Jeanne wanting to go to the wars. Out of innocence the child had spoken. She probably had been mulling over in her mind the conversations she heard when strangers spent a night under their roof. And, dear knows, sighed her mother, there was plenty to fret about in the news one heard from time to time. The miseries prevalent in the awful times of the Black Death, three-quarters of a century gone, were still felt; so much good land lying derelict since those dark days—the plague-haunted, famine-stricken peasantry long since dead or fled; so many dying unshriven, then and since, for want of pastors; so many churches, convents and monasteries fallen to ruin, their congregations scattered, their benefactors no more, the Mass no longer offered on their altars, the Divine Office no longer chanted within their walls. Nay, was not the Church itself disrupted by the Great Schism, and Christians, bewildered, knew not where to turn—to Rome or Avignon. Dreadful tales were told—had she not heard them at her own fireside—of the sorcery and divination being practised by high and low; black magic was rife even in the most Christian land of France. As for other lands, had not a great lady been whipped through the streets of London for casting spells on the King of England; and in Iberia were they not obsessed with wild dreams—'twas said that their navigators had fantastic visions of far horizons beyond the Western Main, where the mountains gleamed with gold and the plains with silver.

Isabel Romée sighed. Life was so hard. Here in France small peasant farmers like those in Lorraine were taxed almost beyond endurance. Things never seemed to get any easier; always more and more taxes to be met. When Louis of Orleans was alive, many blamed him and the Queen, whose favourite he was; then, in turn, people blamed Burgundy; all the time they blamed the English. There was no prosperity, no peace, no good times for honest, hard-working folk since the poor king lost his reason; the invaders, those rough islanders from England, who had come in almost with the Black Death, ravaged the fertile provinces they overran; areas to which they had not yet penetrated were in even worse plight, torn as they were by the never-ending feuds between Armagnacs and Burgundians; and the Grand Companies pillaged wherever they pleased, now that law and order were at a discount. . . . And her poor simple Jeanne would ride out into such a world. . . . Over her mother's dead body, she would!

Jeanne rested on her hoe and looked about the garden. Little square plots of vegetables—carrots and parsnips, beets and radishes, cress and garlic, shallots and parsley— made a draught-board pattern of the space between her father's house and the church. By the wall medlars, quinces, pears and figs ripened in the autumn sun. Gillyflowers brightened the patch by the church wall. The herb garden looked untidy to the uninitiated, but all Isabel's family knew just where each little clump began and ended; the mints—spearmint, peppermint, catmint, pennyroyal; the sweet-smelling lavender and basil; the bitter-leafed rue and dragon's-wort and tansy; the hyssop and sage and saffron. There was not an herb-garden in the whole countryside like theirs, Jeanne reflected; when neighbours' children had the colic, her mother could be relied upon for a bottle of dill-water fresh-brewed from her own dill seeds; at Easter all Domrémy and Greux—and even Maxey—called looking for tansy to flavour the Simnel cakes; and in the two little churches of their valley—too poor for the frankincenses of Arabia—countless tiny thuribles of lavender and mignonette wafted sweet fragrances to the All-Holy Who had pitched His tent therein.

Even as her mother sighed, sitting indoors, Jeanne sighed as she laid down her hoe. She had tried to tell them. She had only half-started when her father began his harangue. She had felt inclined to reveal all to her her mother afterwards, but it was no use. None of them would understand. Worse still, none of them would believe her. How tell of the great Archangel—her friend, her protector, he who was the special protector of France—Michael, the sun-bright one who had had speech with her so often? They would forbid her to go to the woods again, when she told of how he had come there, shining through the tall trees, the sun paling beside the splendour of his raiment. Who would believe her when she spoke of Gabriel or of the myriad angel-presences who had come so close, clustering like wreaths of snow-flakes on the blue air, adapting their greatness to her littleness? Who would listen to her when she told of Catherine and Margaret, those holy ones with crowns so wondrous fair, who had conversed with her and given her heavenly counsel? And if she revealed how it was

four years since first those Voices had called, oh, so softly
. . . just here in the garden by the church . . . as the
noon-tide *Ave* rang . . . they would surely say that she
was a liar and a dissembler.

She laid down the hoe and walked slowly into the
church, her bare feet making no sound on the flagged
floor. Kneeling near the entrance, she wrestled with her
problem. In the beginning, they had only called to her:
"Daughter of God! Daughter of God!"

It was a name she loved to hear, for it told her how
much she meant to God—how intimately she belonged
to Him Who had loved her with an everlasting love.
When her lips replied: "My Father!" her heart told Him
that He was more than father, more than mother, more
than France. In the early apparitions her eyes had tried
to pierce the radiance of the two saints, the splendour of
the Archangel, straining past them to glimpse that beauty
dwelling in the regions of light inaccessible, the reflec-
tion of Whose Countenance made His ambassadors to
glow like the rising sun. When they called "Daughter of
God!" she had been wont to listen intently, hoping to
hear in their tones some echo of that Voice long lost
upon the earth. When the vision paled and vanished, her
hands held on to the bright hems of heavenly garments
until there remained nothing but the dim and empty air,
and—all forlorn—she reached upwards, yearning to clasp
the strong Hand of that unseen Father, the Almighty,
Eternal God Who had called her by the dear name of
Daughter. Later, this longing of the senses ebbed away;
it sufficed to know that she was greatly loved; that she
had found in God a protection and care greater than that

of all fathers since Adam—a love surpassing in tenderness and generosity that of all the mothers in the world.

Then there were the happy days when she learned to pray—to pray like the Angel, her body prostrate on the ground, learning abasement, adoration and the joy of praise from the mighty spirit of Blessed Michael hovering between earth and heaven; humble, reverent and holy, he glorified the Triune God Who gave him being; she learned to pray like the two saints, Catherine and Margaret, now forever singing the mercies of the Lord, blessing Him, loving Him, thanking Him again and again, begging Him to have pity on the realm of France, which had given Him so many of His saints, weeping over the crimes that bred like maggots in the miseries of the times. Thus she prayed for a while now, seeking solace, forgetting worry. Then the more recent behests of her Voices came to trouble her anew; of late they had been more explicit—and more urgent. "Go to France," they had ordered, "go to the Dauphin." Again and again they reproached her: "Why do you tarry? France is in dire need."

Last spring they had clearly told her to go to Robert Baudricourt, the captain of the nearest walled town—Vaucouleurs. "He will give you men-at-arms," they had told her, "he will give you safe escort to the Dauphin. You are the one who will have the Dauphin crowned and anointed King of France in the cathedral of St. Remys." And what had happened? She had persuaded "Uncle" Laxart, on her visit to him and cousin Jeanne last May, to fetch her to the governor of Vaucouleurs (oh, if her father got to hear of that expedition, whatever would he do to her!), and Robert Baudricourt had made sport of herself and her uncle, jesting with his soldiers in such unseemly fashion that good "Uncle" Laxart's neck and ears burned. "The wench is crazy," was the Captain of Vaucouleurs' final word. "Take her home and have her ears boxed."

Remembering the remarks of the governor as he bluntly stated that he and his men-at-arms had but one use for lasses willing to ride to the wars, her own cheeks flamed afresh, kneeling in the little church. . . . Perhaps the Voices were not from Heaven, after all. . . . Yet, they had always urged her to pray well and live well; they had taught her how to pray—surely the Evil One would not do that. . . . But, when she did as they had bidden her, everything went wrong. Lifting her head from her hands she gazed long and steadfastly on the tabernacle; she did not have to voice her uncertainties to the Silent One there. He knew. She did not know how long she knelt; she never knew what time was when she was in the Presence of the Blessed Sacrament. . . . Suddenly, there was the great light again, and they were there . . . they were speaking: "Why do you tarry? Daughter of God, go. Go to the Dauphin." She saw herself, a poor, ill-clad peasant girl; this old red kirtle that had once belonged to her dead sister—how could one go before grand folk in such a wretched garment— but it was all she had. She wept from sheer perplexity. "I am ill-fitted," she faltered. "I cannot mount or ride a horse. I know naught of war." But they insisted. "Go to Baudricourt; he will give you safe conduct." Ah, but see how Baudricourt had treated her before. . . . "Daughter of God, go!"

. . . . .

All through the late autumn and into winter, the Voices urged her on, growing more insistent each time they spoke. It was on Holy Innocents' Day that "Uncle" Laxart came, hurrying, asking for her to come to his wife, Jeanne, whose time was come. Early in the grey morning he came, his sabots echoing along the frost-rutted road until they paused at Jacques' house and began kicking the oaken door, wakening Isabel, who hurried to call Jeanne to make ready and go. It was a matter of minutes for her to don the old dress, patched in three places, to shuffle into her sabots and throw over her shoulders the knitted wrap that she and her mother shared in common. No time was wasted in farewells; there was need for haste, Durand Laxart being a bit doubtful as to whether the old woman he had fetched to his wife would be able to cope with whatever difficulties might arise; he was sorry he had not roused other neighbouring women, and he was anxious to get back as soon as possible. . . . One never knew. . . .

"Uncle" Laxart walked along with quick, jerky steps; Jeanne, who had stopped for a minute to call "Goodbye" to the Guillemette family and again for a word with her friend Mengette, found herself out of breath trying to overtake him. She would have liked to bid farewell to Hauviette, her special friend, the one in whose company she had made her first Holy Communion, but she knew that Durand was worried and so, though Hauviette was dearer to her than anyone in Domrémy and though her heart smote her for leaving her friend without a word, she clip-clopped alongside her relative, silent as he—their breaths floating before them on the cold air that made their fingers tingle and their eyes water. In the Bois Chenu a boar-hunt was in full cry. The horns of the huntsmen sounded clear and the baying of the dogs, now hoarse, now raised in excitement, came to the ears of the pair walking along the Langres road; through the bare, tawny-topped trees one could catch glimpses of the boarhounds—some white, some chestnut—as they dashed from glade to glade and from thicket to thicket. "Uncle" Laxart recalled the good old days when he was a lad and had tramped all one St. Stephen's Day and half the next night to see the Orleans boarhounds and greyhounds being led in procession to the special Mass and Blessing held for them each year; Duke Louis had the priests say a votive Mass and offer prayers that madness be averted from his hunting-packs.

It was when they turned at the bend of the road just beyond the Bois Chenu, that Jeanne realised that she had not looked back for a last look at Domrémy. Her common-sense told her that when the Laxart household had got used to the expected new-comer, she would, of course, come back to her own home. But her sabots, as they hurried along the ice-bound road, beat time to what her heart kept repeating: "Domrémy, farewell! Domrémy, farewell!"

Further along the road a swineherd was driving his hogs, well-fattened after their months spent in the oak-woods, to his master's home. Soon the long-snouted, bristling beasts would be salted away for early spring fare. Durant Laxart commented on the good condition of the swine. They would fetch a fine price at the

Candlemas fairs. People said that the strangers who came to bid at all the recent fairs were sent by the commanders of the various armies to buy provisions for the men under arms. But it was doubtful if even a quarter of the victuals so bought ever reached the soldiers; those who had money were ready and eager to buy from the middlemen—at fancy prices, too. Thus the wealthy feasted, the middlemen grew rich, while the soldiers went hungry.

Jeanne d'Arc hardly heard him. Mention of war was enough to send her thoughts swinging back to their favourite theme—France. For the rest of the journey she resumed her prayer for her country—a prayer that was by now continuous, scarcely interrupted by the happenings of life. As she clip-clopped along, she begged the good God to send France saints, saints whose holiness would be like a bright flag that all the people would follow. St. Vincent Ferrer was dead; after all, he was not a Frenchman but a Spaniard; but he had been a great saint and all France had hearkened to him. True, there was the Blessed Colette, but she was only a woman. What France needed was a different kind of saint for the different sort of bad times that had come upon the land. God knew that there was need of a great man who would be, at the same time, a leader; a holy man, strong in hope, shining like a beacon over the hopelessness that was France; surely God would not refuse the pleadings of the hosts of chosen souls that France had given Him to people Heaven; to their pleadings Jeanne d'Arc joined hers. All the way to Burey-le-Petit she prayed that it might not be long before God sent a saint, such a one as the times needed, a saint-leader who would end the temporal miseries and the spiritual famine of the people.

Chapter Three

L E SIRE DE BAUDRICOURT had just returned from his
morning ride around the walled town of Vaucouleurs.
He was well pleased with life—his life. Had he not kept
the Dauphin's flag flying over Vaucouleurs when others
had given in to Burgundy, or to the English, or to turn-
coats like the de Vergys, who veered with every wind?
Alone of all the captains of the border country he had
not only held his own and made the *villenie* of Vaucouleurs as a little isle of loyalty in an area controlled
partly by alien, partly by traitor authority, but he had
made many a foray against the various enemies when
occasion offered. He was a rough, hearty man, blunt-
spoken and unenthusiastic by nature, but with a shrewd
calculating turn of mind when faced with problems in-
volving mercenary matters. There had been no little
gossip in the locality over Robert's matrimonial affairs;
his choice of a rich widow for second wife might have
caused no comment if his first wife had not also been
a rich widow. A tough, unsentimental soldier, his

loyalty and his sense of humour made the governor of Vaucouleurs more popular than most governors.

Swinging off his horse, he flung the reins to a man-at-arms and stamped into the courtyard. It was the 19th of February, in the year of Our Lord 1429; just a week since that Domrémy wench had rushed into this same courtyard like one demented, with a daft story of some dire misfortune that had befallen the Dauphin's men at Orleans; he, the King's Captain, had, of course, pooh-poohed such wild talk. It was disconcerting to find out afterwards that Jean of Metz and Bertrand Poulengy, two of his best squires, averred that they firmly believed everything this Jeanne d'Arc said. Jean of Metz told of how he had called at the wheelwright's house where the maid abode. The wheelwright, Henri Rover, and his wife Catherine, were loud in praise of the girl who had lodged with them these three weeks past; she spun well and she stitched beautifully, Catherine Royer said; and spent her spare time praying. One day when Henri and his wife had been speaking of the Queen, the wretched Isabelle of Bavaria, she gave them both something of a shock when she looked up from the spindle and asked, in all earnestness: "Have you not heard of the old saying that France should be lost by a woman and restored by a maiden from the marches of Lorraine?" There *was* such an old saying; everyone in France knew it, but it gave the Royers a jolt to hear the Lorraine girl repeat it; somehow, on her lips it had some strange new significance.

Jean of Metz said that they had hardly finished telling him of this, when Jeanne herself had entered, clad in her poor, red, much-patched kirtle; he had thought to rally her. "*Ma mie!*" he cried, "what are you doing here then? Methought you would have long since hied to the aid of the King. Or must we all turn English?" Jeanne had replied very gravely: "I have come to this royalist town to ask Robert Baudricourt to lead me to the King. He heeds me not. None the less I must be with the Dauphin by mid-Lent, though I wear my legs to the knees. No one on earth, neither King, nor Duke, nor the King of Scotland's daughter, nor anyone else can recover the realm of France; nor is there any succour save through me, though I would fain stay by my mother's side, since I am ill-fitted to this task. Yet go I must, and those things must I do, for so wills my Lord." Jean of Metz had seldom heard such noble speech on the lips of so earnest and, withal, so humble a maid. Her Lord? Who could he be? Not that old reprobate, Charles of Lorraine? His son-in-law, mayhap, René of Bar, whose duchy was being so unmercifully harried from both sides?

"Who is he—your Lord?" he had asked.

"Who is my Lord?" she had repeated, as though astonished that all did not know where her allegiance lay. "My Lord is God."

And Jean of Metz, telling the tale afterwards to Captain Robert and the others at the garrison, had added, half-shyly, half-proudly: "I took her hand, as did Poulengy in turn, and swore by my faith in the living God and by my honour as a soldier of the King, that I would lead her to the Dauphin." The only thing he wished to know was when she wanted to start.

"Today, rather than tomorrow," she had replied, "but better tomorrow than the day after."

So, when she had rushed in on the 12th of February, bewailing a disaster which she said had befallen that very day near Orleans, Jean of Metz and Poulengy—and indeed, others—had hung on her words; their very bearing seemed to say What-did-I-tell-you! Today had brought no tidings from Orleans; it would take about nine days for news to travel from Orleans to Vaucouleurs, even bad news, a proverbially fast traveller. Robert Baudricourt frowned to himself; it was difficult to know how to handle this affair of Jeanne d'Arc. Last year he had given herself and her fool of a relative, the one she called "Uncle" Laxart, short shrift, and had hoped that the matter was ended. But with the new year, trouble returned in the shape of the same lass from Domrémy. Now, all Vaucouleurs was humming with talk about the girl; if she were one giving cause for scandal or even suspicious gossip, it would be easy to deal with her—he would have her whipped down the winding hill from the castle and through the narrow streets of the town, and that would settle matters! But, before it was light, was she not seen, in the raw mornings of mid-winter, wending her way to the chapel yonder? And there were stories told of Mass-servers finding her waiting there, or in the crypt below, at the Shrine of Our Lady of France, her face brighter than the dawn breaking the gloom on the eastern hills.

Another horseman came clattering into the courtyard, rousing the Captain of Vaucouleurs from his preoccupation with this problem of how to deal with Jeanne d'Arc;

a King's messenger, by Heaven, and one who had ridden hard, judging by his spattered cloak and sweating mount; maybe the Dauphin was sending aid to Vaucouleurs, the only one left of the eight loyalist fortresses in the West; the only border outpost whose captain had kept faith with his King and held all foes at bay.

"What news?" he asked abruptly. Only courtiers wasted time in silly greetings that meant nothing.

"The worst," replied the other. "Near Orleans, just this day last week, the Saturday before Ash Wednesday, of all ill days ever, the English made a laughing-stock of our army, routing us completely. La Hire had laid brave plans to march with an army of Orleanists and intercept a convoy of dried herrings and other Lenten fare that one Sir John Falstaff and the Provost of Paris were bringing to the English army besieging Orleans." The messenger took breath and continued his narrative: "The convoy was long and straggling, three hundred wagons 'twas said, and La Hire ascertained that there were but fifteen hundred English and Burgundian troops riding with the herring-wagons."

"Fifteen hundred! Say not that fifteen hundred *Goddams* routed the French!" Baudricourt sounded as though he could not credit his hearing. The garrison gathered to listen to the incredible news.

"Another army of Dauphin's men butted in. Would that they had left matters to La Hire! That headstrong Charles of Bourbon, the young count of Clermont, thinking, no doubt, that he himself might achieve some glory in the victory—which appeared to be a foregone conclusion—had command of the second army, and was

to come on Falstaff and the convoy at the same time as
La Hire." The messenger paused, overcome by the bit-
terness of the defeat as much as by his own weariness; a
squire passed him the tankard from which he himself had
been drinking; he took a few gulps, wiped his cloak
across his mouth, and continued:

"Clermont—may he never see another of his name!—
gave orders and counter-orders until his men didn't
know whether they were advancing or retreating; he
delayed so long that La Hire could hold in the unruly
Orleanists no longer and they attacked; but by this time
Falstaff, who saw that his only chance was to draw up
the wagons and fight from behind them, had his men
ready and in good array; fighting for their lives they
were and they knew it; the Orleanists broke lines on
coming to the wagons and the *Goddams* just cut them
in pieces."

"But what of Clermont?" interrupted a man-at-arms.

"The accursed coward came up just in time to see the
disaster and, instead of going to help La Hire, who was
fighting like the devil to rally his men, he fled in confusion to Orleans. Though his force alone far outnum-
bered Falstaff's, mark you."

Consternation, shame, rage and despair showed on the
faces of the garrison-men of Vaucouleurs. Jean of Metz
stared his captain full in the eyes.

"It is as she said—*la bonne Lorraine*," he said. The
men-at-arms and the squires fell to whispering; Baudricourt drew the King's messenger aside; he did not wish
his words overheard.

"They speak of the lass I mentioned in the letter I sent the Dauphin last month," he explained.

"I had almost forgotten," murmured the other. "I bring orders that she is to be sent to the Court at Chinon; some say that now Talbot's in Orleans, our only hope is heavenly aid—if she *is* of Heaven, this one from Domrémy. Some say that they are ready to accept help from even a witch—should she prove a witch."

"What says the Dauphin?"

"He's curious. Anything to relieve the boredom of court life. He says that you are to send her back when I ride again for Chinon. This is Saturday. I start for Chinon on Wednesday. Can she be ready then? We will need an escort to ride with us."

"She will be ready," said the Captain, brusquely, rising and striding away. He moved towards the chapel. Why had he not thought of this before? By Heaven, he was not going to have a wench from that sleepy little village of Domrémy make a laughing-stock of him before the courtiers in Chinon. Before letting her go, he would fetch the *curé*, Jean Fournier, to her; soon all would know if she were bewitched by the Evil One.

The *curé* heard him patiently.

"You wish me to exorcise her now?"

"Now. Before she is warned by anyone that such is to be done. I will come with you. Make haste."

The *curé* reached for the stole hanging on the wall; he hastily thumbed through a sheaf of parchment leaves until he found the one he needed; he had a crucifix, a little flask with holy water and a piece of blessed candle in his satchel; so often was one called in a hurry these times to give the last rites, it behoved a priest to be ready always. Already Baudricourt was outside, impatient to get through with the business he had just decided upon. The *curé* hastened to overtake him: soon they were at the Royers' house.

"Leave us," ordered Baudricourt. Catherine Royer rose from her seat by the fire, and with an uneasy glance at her young lodger, a curtsey for the Governor and a frightened bow towards the priest, went into the adjoining room; there was a crack in the door, and Madame Royer, without any qualms of conscience, immediately pressed her forehead against the timbers, slewing her head up and down until she obtained as good a view as possible of the kitchen and its occupants.

Jeanne d'Arc had risen on their entrance, but had not moved from her position in the corner by the fire; her eyes were on the *curé*, who had put on his stole, lit a blessed candle and was sprinkling holy water into the four corners of the little room. He was speaking now, and to Jeanne. Catherine Royer could not quite make out the words; it was like the start of Mass. *"In Nomine Patris, et Filii, et Spiritus Sancti!* I adjure thee, if thou art an evil thing, to keep away, but if thou art good I adjure thee to approach hither."

You could hear the *curé* breathing—and the Captain, too, Catherine Royer said afterwards, telling her friends; as for herself, her heart just hammered with great, heavy thumps until she thought she should have suffocated. But Jeanne only smiled, that strange, slow smile that was more of sadness than of joy; then, she knelt and went across the stone floor towards the priest, on her knees all the way, her eyes fixed neither on Captain nor *curé*, but on the crucifix in the hands of the latter. "You need not kneel, my child," said the *curé*, turning to put away his crucifix and candle; when he had carefully tightened the stopper in the little holy-water flask and folded his stole, he turned to Baudricourt. "Well?" he queried. But the Captain was still wrestling with his problem; he stared stonily at the Maid from Lorraine; perhaps it would be as well to send her on to Chinon; she could hardly make things any worse than they were; but—a farm girl in an old kirtle of red fustian—what a one for the Captain of Vaucouleurs to despatch to his liege lord as a helper in time of need. . . . Madame Royer opened the bedroom door gingerly and, seeing that no one bade her stay where she was, edged into the kitchen again.

There was a step outside, and Jean of Metz appeared in the doorway. "This defeat at Rouvray," he began, " 'the Battle of Herrings,' the *Goddams* are calling it, is the end for France, the King's messenger says. . . . He wishes to see you before he retires, good Baudricourt; he has to arrange about his return to Chinon."

Baudricourt turned and walked away, not waiting for the *curé*, who followed him. "It was as you said," Jean of Metz told Jeanne, "our side was cut to pieces. It seems hopeless to fight any more now, but I am here, Maid, to swear to you that, God helping me, I will give you safe conduct to the Dauphin." And to Madame Royer's amazement, the young soldier swore by his sword, and put his hand into Jeanne's hands as earnestly as though he knelt before his King. "Bertrand is here, too," he said, going to the low doorway and beckoning to Poulengy, who had evidently been waiting outside for quite some time. Poulengy, in his middle thirties, was somewhat older than Jean of Metz; he also, kneeling in the dark kitchen, swore fealty to the Maid, kissing his sword-hilt as he finished. Rising, he turned to Jeanne. "What did the Captain want? And the *curé?*" he asked. Madame Royer could not stay out of things any longer. "He—the Captain—he brought the *curé* to exorcise her," she explained. "Ha, but he got a sorry disappointment if he expected to see Jeanne froth at the mouth, or throw herself on the floor howling like a were-wolf."

"Why did you endure it?" demanded Poulengy, tersely.

"Yes," put in Catherine Royer, "and go along the floor on your knees to the *curé*—why should you lower yourself like that, for no reason at all?"

"I went on my knees because I approached the crucifix —and indeed to honour my Lord in His priest and to show obedience . . . but . . ." Jeanne's voice grew troubled, "the *curé* knew. Has he not heard me in confession not once but many times since I came here? He——"

Jean of Metz could not bear the hurt in her voice. "Of course he knew you were no witch nor the plaything of the Evil One; but he could give no sign of what you told him in confession."

"We waste time." Poulengy was grave. "There are many things to be decided if we ride to Chinon on Wednesday. Jeanne cannot ride in an old red dress, Madame Royer, and we thought—Jean and I thought—"

"I know," cried Catherine, glad of the fuss his words

promised, "I know the very thing for her; the Demoiselle de Coummercy, who has heard of Jeanne and believes in her, she would surely loan her fine costume—the one she wears when out hawking—to Jeanne, a splendid fur-lined *houppelande* with dagged sleeves, and a fur turban with three fine feathers that sweep up from one's brow!"

Jeanne remembered the costume. She had seen the lady of Coummercy last August, wearing that same costume. She herself had been binding the sheaves of wheat that fell before the scythes of her father and Jean; Jacquemin had tied sheaves, too, while Pierre gleaned stray straws here and there amid the stubble. Pierre saw the gay cavalcade first and called to the others; Jean had almost missed seeing such a fine sight, having gone to take a dip in the river nearby. The falconer came first, on foot, with a dead bird at his belt as a decoy, and two fierce hunting-hawks on his wrist; he called to his dogs whenever they forgot their business—the tracking of the game, hares or pheasants; there was a gentleman with a lady riding behind him—not the Demoiselle, she had her own mount—a lady who kept whispering into her companion's ear, so that he made a poor show when he went to let loose his falcon; but Jeanne remembered the Demoiselle and every detail of that hunting outfit. How would it feel to doff this shabby old kirtle, that was poor-looking even in Domrémy, and don such wonderful garments? As yet she did not realise that when she put away the clothing which went with her station in life up to the present, she was also putting away the old way of living.

Poulengy was speaking again; Jean of Metz was frowning at Madame Royer.

"That is not what we thought, Jean and I. If she is to ride all the way to Chinon with Metz and me, the King's messenger, that glum Richard the Archer, and one or two others, she must have suitable attire. Fine garments would attract notice on the way. The best thing she could do is to dress as one of us."

"Fie! For shame, Bertrand Poulengy! Would you have the maid don hose and jerkin and doublet?"

"We have made arrangements already. Jeanne's cousin Durand Laxart, your husband Henri Royer, and a few others of us have put up what money we could, and the citizens of Vaucouleurs are all anxious to help. The cobbler and the seamstress are coming along in an hour to take measurements; they will work day and night if needs be."

"And we have bought a horse for sixteen francs," added Jean of Metz. Jeanne swallowed her disappointment. It was so good to be really allowed to go to the Dauphin at last, that she would have been glad to go dressed as a leper, ringing a Lazarus bell, with a cap drawn down over her face and a few old clouts—the cast-offs of beggars—about her; still, it would have been wonderful to have worn the Demoiselle's hunting-dress, if only for a day. . . . But the horse! "What sort of a horse did you buy for sixteen francs?" she demanded. "He can't be much."

"And what about the black horse the Duke of Lorraine gave her? Heaven knows Henri and I have lost our sleep listening to the great brute champing in his stall every night for the past week; half the work-shop had to be cleared to make way for him."

"The Duke of Lorraine!" Bertrand Poulengy spoke the name with scorn. "With his present of four francs to pay Jeanne's expenses! You may be sure there's something wrong with the horse. Is not the Duke a supporter of the English and Burgundy? I was against her going to his palace at Nancy at all."

"Did he say why he sent for you?" asked Jean of Metz.

"No." The girl was loath to speak of the trip she had made earlier that week.

"What did he say? How did he receive you? You never told us."

"He's lying abed, Bertrand, you know; he's not well."

"You needn't tell us; his sins have caught up with him; everyone knows the life Charles of Lorraine led—and still leads."

" 'Uncle' Laxart came with me all the way. But when we came to the palace it was I who was taken to the Duke; he was in great pain. He said: 'So! You are the one who would go aid the Dauphin against the English. Is all that I hear about you true?' I said: 'What you have said is true, Sire. I can scarce wait for the day when I shall be with the Dauphin.' Then he made a great grimace and asked: 'Can you ride a charger or break a lance?' And I made reply: 'Sire, with the help of God I shall do both.' Then he enquired of me whether he would be cured of his illness or no, but I told him that I had no knowledge of such things, that my Voices when they spoke, spoke only of France and the aid I must bring our land; and I took courage and asked him to enlist his son-in-law René as my helper."

"What said he to that?"

"He pretended not to hear. Maybe he did not hear. He thought of himself only—and his illness. The next words he said were: 'Shall I ever be cured? What must I do to be cured?' I do not know how I knew such things or how I brought myself to answer as I did; I told him that he could not hope to recover while he continued living as he did, sinning openly before God and before all his subjects; I asked him to cease from sin, to put away Alison Dumay and to bring back his Duchess."

"You did!" Jean of Metz gave a sigh of admiration. "I'll wager no one ever spoke to old Lorraine like that before in all his sixty-three years, and came away from Nancy alive! Did he have further speech with you?"

"No. I told him that if he would help my cause I would pray for his return to health—provided that he amended his way of living. It was then that he bade his almoner give me four francs; when we were coming out the palace gates, a stable-man was waiting with the horse."

"Be sure that there's bad blood in that brute," observed Poulengy. "That black was probably in the wars—and not ridden by any of our men either. I'm heartily glad that we bought you this other; though for the life of me I don't know how it will go with us on the long ride to Chinon, if we have to carry you pillion all the way. If you never rode before, you might get thrown, or left behind if we were ambushed and had to ride for our lives."

"Look you! Here comes the seamstress. Leave the clothes to us and you see to any other preparations that must be made." Jeanne was impatient; but Poulengy had

not said all. "Listen!" he ordered. "Madame Royer! See
that her hair is cut short—like a page's; she must have a
man's tunic of dark-grey stuff, a black doublet and a
black cap; the cobbler will see to riding-boots and the
harness-maker will fetch the horse and make adjustments
to the riding accoutrements—though I doubt that the
animal will be needed at all, seeing that she has never
ridden before. Come, Metz, there will be many things to
be seen to, and the time is short."

They went out, bending their heads to avoid hitting
the low lintel. Catherine Royer smiled at her lodger.

"Well . . . you were right again. The Governor *did*
set store on the fact that Duke Charles sent for you."

"Yes; it was as I told you. He sent word to the
Dauphin that I had been summoned to the court at
Nancy; and the Dauphin sent word back that I was to be
sent to him at Chinon. Oh, Catherine! It is so near now,
the time I have so longed for; and yet, the hours between
this and Wednesday will seem the longest of all. Cousin
Jeanne, before her little one came, was impatient and
said that time seemed to drag by—it is like that with me,
only more so; my heart is so eager and the cause is so
urgent."

.   .   .   .   .

It was late afternoon on Wednesday, February 23rd,
1429. The good citizens of Vaucouleurs had gathered in
force outside the Royers' house, full of excitement at the
thought of the brave venture and glowing with pride in
the Maid. They jostled one another, craning heads to see
her come out of Royers' in the clothes they had had
made for her. The Captain had presented her with a

sword, and now stood by, holding her mount, while he talked unconcernedly with the King's messenger. Bertrand Poulengy and Jean of Metz, on their richly-caparisoned horses, struck a bright note in the dull February evening. They wore fur-lined surcoats and Metz had a gay feather in his *capuchon*. Their two serving-men wore their masters' colours and carried their devices on silken pennants; and Richard the Archer, silent as ever, made up the six who were to escort *la bonne Lorraine* the hundred-and-twenty leagues to Chinon.

There was a stir as Jeanne came out. Robert Baudricourt caught his breath. It was a good thought of Poulengy's to have the Maid dress as a page. By Heaven, she made a fine page. In that shapeless kirtle she had looked stocky, but in this suit of black and grey, she seemed tall and lissom, and held her head and shoulders like some lad of the blood royal. The crowd were entranced.

"It's a leather jacket they've made for her," said one, "all laced up the front and tight-fitting; and see the woollen hose—laced to the jacket."

"Some task undoing all those laces and eyelets," said another.

"There are the shoes I set up all night to finish," the cobbler proudly indicated his handiwork, "pointed boots of soft fine leather with spurs attached. Though maybe the spurs won't be wanted. They say she never mounted a horse before, much less rode one."

Baudricourt walked to where Jeanne stood. "Your horse, Maid. Will you mount now?"

Jeanne nodded. There was a general hush and all eyes

centred on the horse that had cost sixteen francs and on the one who was to ride him. It was done in an instant without any help from Poulengy or Metz, who were standing anxiously by, ready to lend a hand; now she had one foot in the stirrup, now she had swung into the saddle—up and sitting easily as though she had been long accustomed to it. . . . Her hat, a *capuchon* with ends which fell scarf-like about her shoulders, seemed to be troublesome, so she snatched it off and thrust it in her saddle-bag. The wind played with her hair, cut short, just reaching the level of her chin.

They were making ready to start. "The blessing," she said, with a reproving look at Metz and Poulengy. All swung to the ground again; the men stood by their mounts, Jeanne knelt on the ground. The *curé*, who had emerged from the Royers' doorway, gave his special blessing and recited verses from the Psalms:

> *Though I should walk in the midst of the shadow of death, I will fear no evil, for Thou art with me, O Lord. . . . Direct my steps according to Thy word; and let no iniquity have dominion over me. . . . God hath given His angels charge over thee, to keep thee in all thy ways. . . . Thou shalt walk upon the asp and the basilisk and thou shalt trample underfoot the lion and the dragon. . . . Perfect Thou my goings in Thy paths, that my footsteps be not moved. . . .*

"It grows late," said the King's messenger; "we travel by night, and sleep by day; it's the safest way, Maid. Will you lead on now? We ride out by the Porte de France."

"Have a care, Maid," called a citizen. "There are men of blood on every road you ride."

"I do not fear them," replied Jeanne, "my way lies straight before me: and if I meet them face-to-face I have Him with me Whose way no man dare block. He will make clear my road to the Dauphin. Let us go to aid the Dauphin and France. . . . For this was I born." And, swinging into the saddle again, she rode into the sunset, towards the west wall of Vaucouleurs. The crowd gave a cheer; Catherine Royer wept and smiled by turns; the *curé* kept repeating to himself her last words; they were the very words Another had used: "For this was I born. . . ."

The little cavalcade made a halt at the castle, where the Captain made each man of the escort swear to conduct the Maid safe to Chinon. He said no farewells, for he had not much faith in the enterprise. Robert Baudricourt was no courtier with ready speech and facile compliments, but they were evidently expecting him to say something before they moved off. Well—he would say what the Voices had said: "Va . . . Go!" "Go—whatever be the outcome," he cried, gesturing them to be on their way. The horses clattered over the cobblestones. Out under the Porte de France, with the King's messenger leading now, setting a good smart pace. Out the Gate of France and down the hillside, with the cheers of the crowd ringing in their ears. The Maid rode as well as the best, thought Jean of Metz, as he hummed to himself a song, every verse of which ended with:

> Chinon on the blue Vienne,
> Four hundred miles away.

Chapter Four

MANY RUMOURS ran through France in that Lent of
1429; news of wars and yet more wars; tales of
Popes and anti-Popes; tidings good and tidings evil. But
one strange rumour travelled swifter than any; and it
gained as it went, as rumours are wont to do. They were
saying that a maiden named Jeanne from some remote
village in Lorraine—from the very back of beyond—was
riding into the heart of France, riding to the Dauphin, to
lead an army against the enemies of the realm. She had
had Heavenly visions, this peasant maid, and those saints
whom France had ever honoured had bidden *la bonne
Lorraine* to go to the aid of the Dauphin. Some said that
Our Lord Himself had spoken to her; certain it was that
the Protector of France, St. Michael the Archangel, had
appeared to her—sometimes in her father's garden, sometimes in the little chapel where she prayed, oftenest in
the woods near her home; and now she was on her way.
When would she see the Dauphin? Where? How was
she coming? Would the power of Heaven lift her up—

like Habacuc of old—and set her down at her destination? Thus the rumours and the surmises. . . . But there were places where there were no rumours, places where the Maid had been seen in the flesh.

There was the quiet abbey of the Benedictines at St. Urbain on the Marne. The Lord Abbot, kinsman of Robert Baudricourt, had spent the night of February 23rd pacing the cloisters, often going to the Eastern Gate to listen for the noise of galloping hooves. It was almost dawn when the little party arrived, soaked to the skin by the February rains that had swept the hills west of Vaucouleurs; they had their horses' hooves muffled to travel as noiselessly as might be. So it was that when they rode in under the Gothic archway of the great courtyard, no one was there to greet them; but the monks were rising, as Matins had to be sung and the first Masses said before daylight. Soon the travellers were partaking of the hospitality of the monastery. Jeanne was a strange sight in that quiet place; monks passing along the flagged hall-way into the chapel considered the young page who had come in with the last lot of guests very devout; he knelt upright for the space of three Masses and approached the Communion rail with a deep reverence. One would have thought that, like the other weary travellers of his company, he would have seen to bodily refreshment before devoting himself to the things of the spirit. Some noble youth, they surmised, when they saw the Lord Abbot come to escort him from the chapel. It was strange though, that he was taken to the apartments beyond the enclosure, to the cells where the female relatives of the monks, and great ladies who were benefactresses of the monastery were accommodated when they passed a night at St. Urbain.

The Lord Abbot, having shown his guest to her quarters, returned to make arrangements for her escort. Already six beds were being prepared. He spoke but little; it was yet the time of the Great Silence, and he had had to cut short his customary thanksgiving after Mass. The King's messenger was explaining how they had deemed it well to avoid the forest called La Saulxnoire; Heaven knew what cut-throats its dark trees sheltered. Jean of Metz was commenting on the bad state of the roads, the rains that had soaked them, the rivers—sixteen in all to be crossed—that would now be in spate; the waning moon. Poulengy was silent and anxious-looking; the other three only thinking of how soon they might stretch their weary limbs and sleep. If the beds were as good as the food, their first halt would not have been a bad one, whispered Richard the Archer to the two men-at-arms.

The rest was good. Their horses had been well looked after. On the following evening they knelt for the blessing of the Lord Abbot, before riding further into the west.

Poulengy and Jean of Metz rode just behind the Maid. The King's messenger and Richard the Archer were away ahead, galloping fast. There was a huge cave on the western slopes of yonder hill; the messenger had sheltered in it when coming from Chinon. The party could hide in this refuge all next day and get some sleep; the men would take turns at watching.

Jean of Metz had something on his mind. He hemmed

and hawed for half-a-league before he could bring himself to broach the matter to his friend.

"Poulengy, you and I have been through many a skirmish together——"

"What's worrying you, Metz? Knowing what I am where women are concerned, you are afraid that I may be thinking of making unseemly advances to the Maid?"

"Well—yes; I know that you swore to Baudricourt to see her safe to the Dauphin; but she's comely and finely-built, just the sort that used take your fancy in Vaucouleurs and Metz."

"Were it any of the others who compared her to *them*, I would run him through with my sword. But—old comrade—to reassure you, I tell you I would never dare to make any overtures to her that I might to others of her age and appearance."

"Neither would I. But I have no great trust in the Archer, no—nor in the King's man either. Promise me that if aught befalls me on the way, you will guard her—as you would your own sister."

"It's a needless oath, but I swear it just the same. Meanwhile, we three must keep together; when we lie down to sleep she lies between us twain; and keep your sword unsheathed. But she will wonder why we tarry so long behind. Put spurs to your mount and overtake her."

The Maid had a worried look on her usually calm face. Jean of Metz had seldom seen her so—not since the day she had run to Baudricourt with news of the disaster at Rouvray. "How now, Maid!" he rallied, then fell silent. Perhaps she had been taking counsel with her Voices as she rode; they spoke to her in strange places and often at unexpected times. "Will you do as you say—come to the aid of France and the Dauphin?" he asked, anxiously, smitten with sudden doubt. "Fear not," replied Jeanne; "what I do is by command; and my Brothers in Providence have told me that all will be well. But I am sad, Jean. Why cannot we go into one of the village churches we come to, and hear Mass? If only we could hear Mass, all would surely be well."

"This is Anglo-Burgundian country, Maid. We dare not risk it. We are pledged to bring you safe to young Charles at Chinon. You may be sure the old Duke of Lorraine told Philip of Burgundy that you were hoping to reach Chinon by mid-Lent; every road and ford will be watched—not only by the Blue-caps, but by the English, who are well entrenched in these parts. Worst of all are the bands of marauders that infest the whole country, and who would only be too pleased to hold us to ransom, and sell to the highest bidder—and there are thousands of such traitors and knaves even among Frenchmen, who would do anything for gold. But, on Sunday, perhaps we shall be near to Auxerre, the town of St. Germain. There we might mingle with the crowds and not be noticed in the throngs in the Cathedral."

And so it happened. Auxerre was a fair-sized city, belonging to the Duke of Burgundy. Its good citizens had a wholesome fear of all troops, whatever their allegiance; they had learned by experience that bands of armed horsemen were best given a wide berth. When the seven riders, mud-splashed and weary-eyed, flung themselves from their jaded horses and proceeded to Mass in the splendid Cathedral whose lighted windows glowed like jewels in the grey of the morning, no one asked whence they had come or whither they were making for. When later that same day the Duke's soldiers were enquiring if anyone had seen a party of men conveying a maid through the streets, no one had seen such a thing. To be sure there was that party that had heard Mass in the Cathedral that morning, but there was no maid. Would they not have seen her riding pillion?

. . . . .

When they were a couple of nights' journey west of Auxerre, danger threatened; it was close on midnight and they were riding hard, hoping to reach royalist territory by dawn. Richard the Archer and the King's messenger, who had been leading the way, as usual, suddenly pulled up their horses, wheeled, and came back at a good trot.

"What's afoot?" asked Poulengy, anxiously, unsheathing his sword, and signing to Jeanne and the other three to turn and ride back the way they had come.

"Some kind of hunt; we could see torches here and there in the valley yonder; if we ride on we cannot avoid meeting some of the party."

"Aye, there's a crowd of them," confirmed the Archer. "And we thought we heard screaming. It's some human game they're after; maybe someone of the Dauphin's men, with a pack of the *Goddams* or the Burgundy-men at his heels."

"Then in God's name, let us ride to help whoe'er they hunt," urged Jeanne, irritated at the time being lost trotting back over the roads she had been so gladly leaving behind.

"Nay," said the King's messenger. "We know not

whom or what they hunt, Maid. Would you have us all walk into a trap, now that we are so near our goal?"

"There is a thicket in the hollow near the river," pointed out Jean of Metz. "We could be concealed there—horses and all; ten to one the chances are they'll pass on; their game, whate'er or whoe'er it be, won't venture the river at this point, with the floods so high."

It was now too late to debate the question, for, without warning, torches were coming from the west side of the hill. With one accord, the seven riders turned towards the thicket, where they quickly made plans in case of discovery. Jeanne, Jean of Metz and the King's messenger were to remain in the saddle, ready to ride hell-for-leather over the last few miles of enemy country; Poulengy and the men-at-arms and the Archer would fight as long as there was life left in them, to delay the pursuit. In a few minutes they heard a scream—a woman's scream—rise, spend itself and die out in a long piercing "Ai-ai-ai-ai!" It was a good distance away.

"I know what it is," said Poulengy, crossing himself, "a witch-hunt. There must be a coven of witches; they've caught the one who is yelling, and the pricker is working on her. They are hunting in groups trying to lay hands on the others."

Even as he spoke, they heard the laboured breathing of one of the hunted. They remembered the tales of the dreadful things that had happened in Lorraine twenty years before, when the witches had been found dancing around their great stone whereon they had offered the dread sacrifice to Satan—the Witches' Mass—the Black Mass, where the bread and wine and candles were all

black. There was not one man of that little band who
did not call under his breath on the Blessed Name of
Jesus, praying that they might all perish by the steel of
the enemy through whose country they travelled, sooner
than meet up with one of these hags who had power
from the Evil One to send a man out of his wits.

"Christ save us!" muttered one of the men-at-arms,
afraid to look, yet unable to refrain from doing so, as
past the thicket and making for the river, went a wizened
crone, rushing at a speed unbelievable for one so old. Six
shadowy forms, holding their torches aloft, and speaking
directions to one another as they ran, followed her hot-
foot. Not daring to speak or move, the group in the
thicket stayed motionless, each one fearful lest his horse
should stamp or whinny; indeed, it was the horses'
sudden pricking-up of ears that made them aware that
someone else had come in at the opposite side of the
thicket and was edging carefully towards the centre. It
was all the King's messenger could do to hold Richard
the Archer and keep him from bolting into the open,
when the puffing for breath and the muttering of strange
unknown words made it clear that this was another of
the devil's crew. Poulengy, in sign language, indicated
that he was going to run his sword through the witch the
moment she appeared at his side of the clump of bushes.
But Jeanne, moved by sudden pity, signed to him to
desist, and carefully edged her mount to the spot where
the twigs were being crackled, oh, ever so slightly. There
was the witch—glaring at them, her malevolent eyes at
once grasping the situation; these riders were hunted just
as she; so long as she did not cry out or make trouble,

they would not give her away. Her hair hung in glibs about her face; her toothless gums kept mumbling who knew what unspeakable incantations; the riders stared back at her, horror-stricken, inanimate; the horses shivered and grew restive. Only Jeanne was unafraid; she leant over and pulled the flask from her saddle-bag, and handed it to the creature before her: "Drink," she whispered, "and rest. We will not harm you."

The hunt seemed to have gone past them. The Archer ventured to strike a flint. Poulengy nudged Metz. Down the hollow cheeks of the witch tears were slowly coursing. The others saw what Poulengy saw and took heart. Everyone knew that witches did not weep; this one was no witch; some old beldame who had fed crumbs to sparrows during the snow, perhaps, or who had kept a cat or a toad for a pet, and thus drawn suspicion on herself. The King's messenger went out to reconnoitre. In a few minutes he was back to say that the road was clear now, they might proceed. Jeanne left her flask with the old one. "There will be flasks a-plenty when we come to our journey's end," she told Metz, smilingly, glad to be moving for Chinon again.

All along the way for the rest of that night, Poulengy and Metz talked of nothing but witches and witch-hunts they had known. The pricker, he who had caused the first screams they had heard, he had to know his business; to search the witch's person for the Devil's Mark, and when he found it to stab a pin to the head in it. Though other pricks and wounds made on the hag's body might cause bleeding—and thus bring the creature's evil powers to naught—if she were verily a witch, the Devil's Mark

would yield no blood, even though one drove a dagger
to the hilt in it. But there were other tests; a few would
hold her, careful not to let her feet touch the earth once
she had been lifted from it, and others would burn
candles beneath the soles of her feet; if she were a witch
her feet would show never a scorch-mark; but the most
infallible test was the ordeal by water, when, with right
thumb tied to left big toe and left thumb tied to right
big toe, the hag would be cast into the water, while those
on the bank said the appropriate prayers; a witch would
float, of course; an innocent woman would sink and
there would be a rush to dive in to her rescue.

"Desist, friend Bertrand. The Maid has no stomach for
such conversation. She has been silent ever since we left
the thicket." Jean of Metz was always uneasy when
Jeanne remained apart. . . . They were riding through
a village, just at the border. An acrid smell hung in the
air. The smoke of a dead fire floated in the half-light of
dawn. The horses snorted and turned from the sickening
sight at the top of the street, where three cross-roads
met; two blackened butts of stakes still smouldered, mute
monuments to the little heaps of charred remains that lay
beneath. The riders crossed themselves and called on
Christ, His Mother and the blessed saints; they drew
their cloaks up over their mouths and nostrils, and spurred
their horses. . . . The Maid rode alone; she saw ahead
the spires of Gien; they were in loyalist territory. She
should have been happy; and she would have been
happy—if she could forget those blackened stakes standing like sentinels . . . dark sentinels brooding over grim

burdens laid down for ever there where the three roads met.

The night travel ceased now that they were in friendly territory; it was pleasant riding for the last few days, with a touch of spring in the air; with little groups here and there in the hamlets and the towns recognising them and raising a cheer. Once they stopped to enquire from a group of horsemen wearing the Dauphin's colours, what news from Orleans. The news was bad; could not, in fact, be worse; the disaster at Rouvray had made both garrison and citizens despair. Many commanders had slipped away from what they regarded as a doomed city. Even the Bishop had gone.

"Is there no one left to lead the men?" Jeanne asked.

"None worth the name of leader, lady—save le Bâtard d'Orléans; and he lies wounded."

"Where is Clermont?" she demanded, "he who saved his own skin and that of his army at the 'Battle of Herrings,' but struck not a blow to aid La Hire."

"He's deserted; took himself and his army away to Chinon; his disgrace was not counted against him there by all accounts; le Bâtard told him that were it not for the arrow-wound in his foot, he would have much pleasure in speeding his departure with a kick."

"Who is the Bishop of Orleans? Why has he gone?"

"He's a Scot. John Kirkmichael. He's a soldier, too. The people of Orleans would not have minded his going so much—perchance there are many of his kith and kin fighting with Falstaff or Talbot—but for the fact that he made two thousand fighting men decamp with him."

"How are they for food?" asked Poulengy.

"Not so bad since Clermont's army and those who followed the Bishop went away. It is surprising how friends outside manage to smuggle something in every other day; a drove of hogs one morning, a couple of pack-horses laden with kids one evening, twenty-six horned beasts only yesterday."

"We should be going with speed to their aid. Come! Every minute is precious." The Maid was eager to be on her way.

"You said you would visit St. Catherine's shrine at Fierbois," Metz reminded her. "It is only a mile ahead."

The others agreed that Fierbois should be visited. It was Saturday evening; a good night's rest and a chance to brush themselves up before presenting themselves at court would be the proper thing. Besides, Jeanne had yet to dictate her letter to the Dauphin; that could be done this evening and the King's messenger would ride on to Chinon and deliver it before nightfall. There would be many Masses at the shrine on the morrow and, after attending the earliest ones, they could ride on the last six leagues to Chinon.

Jeanne agreed. She had almost forgotten the letter to the Dauphin; as she rode along to visit the shrine of one of her saints, she composed her message to Charles; she would bid her scrivener write thus:

> *I have travelled a hundred and twenty leagues to bring you aid; I am the bearer of good tidings for you; I shall recognise you among any crowd of people.*

.   .   .   .   .

Three Masses followed one another in the little church

of St. Catherine of Fierbois, on the morning of Lætare
Sunday, which in that year fell on March 6th. Jeanne
was happy to be able to be present at all three—happier
still to receive the King of Heaven into her soul. She
prayed so long and so fervently that her little party got
impatient; it was time to ride for Chinon; Poulengy
broke in on her devotions to tell her that the horses were
saddled and all in readiness. If she would partake of the
breakfast prepared, they could start. Recalled to worldly
affairs, the Maid hastened to make ready; she was fasting
for Lent and would not eat until noon.

Sharp, sleety showers stung their cheeks as they rode
along the last lap of their long journey; in between, the
sun shone with a cold, dazzling brilliancy. Back in
Domrémy the children would be trooping out for the
first picnic of the year; out to the big tree by the
fountain—the one that some called the "Ladies' Tree,"
others the "Fairies' Tree"; sometimes the *seigneur* of
Bourlemont and his lady would come and join in the
dances of the children round the fountain and the tree;
there would be songs and everyone would hang little
garlands of the first flowers of spring on the spreading
branches. This year there would be no Jeanne; she had
loved the singing and the dancing, though since the
Voices came, she had never danced—why, she could not
say—but she sang as gaily as any. Would they miss her?
Would they——

"Maid!" called Jean of Metz, excitedly, "look yonder!
Chinon!"

"Well they named it 'White Chinon on the blue

Vienne,'" said Poulengy, shading his eyes the better to admire the city that lodged the Dauphin.

The March sun caught the bastions and towers of the great castle, and made the mullioned windows glitter like gold. The huge building that ran along by the sparkling Vienne dwarfed the little grey-roofed houses of the townsfolk clustered about its base. A bell from some courtyard of the castle began ringing the mid-day Angelus. The travellers halted and uncovered. Poulengy spoke to Jeanne for a moment before they rode on.

"I am anxious, now that we are in Chinon; perhaps we may not be well received. Charles and his councillors may think our mission a fool's errand and send us all packing. And the money collected for us in Vaucouleurs —with the little that Metz and myself had saved—it's all gone. We'll be a nice laughing-stock if we have to return to Baudricourt without a franc between the lot of us, except for the four francs old Lorraine gave you."

"I gave them to the beggars in Auxerre and Gien. But have no fear. The Dauphin will receive us kindly."

Near the church of St. Maurice there was a little inn. There they dined, rested and spruced themselves up, leaving their horses in the adjoining stable. Before sitting down to table, Jeanne sent another note to the Castle, telling the Dauphin of her safe arrival and asking for an immediate audience; Jean of Metz and Poulengy themselves undertook to deliver the missive. But the Dauphin had changed his mind since he sent the messenger posting to Vaucouleurs the previous month. Now he had to have enquiries made about her; in vain did Poulengy and Jean of Metz tell of her goodness and sincerity; of how she saw in vision the "Battle of Herrings," of the wonderful protection they had enjoyed on the long and hazardous trip from Lorraine. Charles was in no hurry; there was other business to be attended to that day and the next; La Trémoille, the Dauphin's favourite, pointed out that it would ill befit royalty to be at the beck and call of any peasant wench—a tomboy, who bestrode her horse and dressed like a man, that was how he had heard *la Lorraine* described. And things were come to a pretty pass when a half-daft young rustic maid could presume to advise His Highness in matters of State.

"Things couldn't be at a worse pass," remarked Charles' mother-in-law, the Queen of Sicily, who could not abide La Trémoille. "If she is all these squires say, she may prove to be a saving grace."

But this was one of the days when La Trémoille's every whim was satisfied, and the Archbishop of Rheims, who was present, thought the favourite's counsel most prudent. The Dauphin, as usual, could not or would not oppose La Trémoille; at the same time he wished to please Yolande of Sicily. As a compromise, he suggested that a deputation visit this Maid at her lodgings, and question her closely.

So several noblemen and gentlemen of the royal household hied them to the inn near the church of St. Maurice. It was a welcome relief from the dull routine of the court, and both the partisans of La Trémoille and the supporters of Yolande hoped to bring back versions of the interview calculated to please their respective patrons.

The wench was stubborn for a long while, refusing to tell anything except to the Dauphin himself; finally she was badgered into saying that the King of Heaven had sent her for the immediate purpose of raising the siege of Orleans; she was then to see that the Dauphin was crowned at Rheims. She wanted men, horses, and arms.

"What arrogance and what madness!" chorused the friends of La Trémoille, as they hastened back to the castle. "The Maid speaks the truth, and is incapable of duplicity," said the allies of Yolande. The Dauphin's confessor, who had taken Jean of Metz and Poulengy aside and questioned them closely about Jeanne's early life, was struck by the fact that she had tended sheep. It was strange the predilection of Heaven for shepherds whenever a direct communication had to be conveyed from God to man, right down from the beginning of time, when the shepherd Abel offered the firstlings of his flock to the Lord God; through the long line of patriarchs from Adam to Noe, and from Noe to Abraham and Isaac and Jacob and on and on and on to Booz and Obed and Jesse and David, the shepherd-boy of Bethlehem. The prophets, too, how many of them had tended flocks—like Amos, whom the Lord took when he followed the flock, saying: *"Go, prophesy to My people Israel."* Shepherds were the first to hear the glad news of the birth of the Saviour. . . . Had not Christ kept for Himself the title of the Good Shepherd? . . . And ever since, the Dauphin's confessor reflected, as he listened to Jeanne answering her questioners, there had certainly been something about shepherds that drew the gaze of Heaven to them; St. Geneviève of Paris; the great St. Patrick of Ireland—but he was forgetting his business; Charles would be anxious for his opinion and, in the long run, he would probably set more store by it than Yolande's or even La Trémoille's.

The courtiers left the inn and hastened back along the cobbled street to the castle. In the room where the Maid had received them there was a long silence. Jean of Metz flicked his riding boots with his whip; Poulengy scowled at nothing in particular; Jeanne stood by the little window, hurt to the heart; the threats of her father, the coarse jests of le Sire de Baudricourt were as nothing compared to this casual reception. She began making excuses for it to herself; it was not the Dauphin, it was the courtiers and the court regulations; it was not fair to blame the courtiers, either—they did not know Who had sent her; it was He Who was not received, and He would probably have been received at once—and right heartily—had He chosen for Himself a better ambassador. Yes, it was hard for gentle folk to think that God would choose a poor peasant girl, unlettered, uncouth in her ways, to come to the rescue of Charles, the gentlest-born of them all. She blinked back her unshed tears and turned to her friends.

"You found him—the Dauphin—in good health?"

"As pale-faced as all the courtiers; and just as spindle-shanked and knock-kneed as the gentlemen of his retinue." Poulengy gave a sardonic grin, then resumed his scowling.

"He wobbles a bit, physically and mentally," confirmed Metz. "He's a most ordinary-looking fellow, this Charles you wish to crown, Maid. Were he to doff his robes of state and mingle with the crowd of courtiers he'd not be noticeable for his kingly mien; indeed, he'd be quite undistinguished-looking and as bored-looking as any there."

"I should know him anywhere. And no matter how great the throng about him, I would single him out," said the Maid.

.   .   .   .   .

It was not until Wednesday evening that she was bidden to the Castle. In the great hall which ran full seventy feet in length along the southern wall of the Château du Milieu, the courtiers, soldiers, councillors, prelates and clerks waited in some excitement. It was well known that the portly favourite, La Trémoille, and the Archbishop of Rheims were totally against this girl from Lorraine; and it was known that Yolande and the King's confessor had visited and spoken with the Maid several times since Sunday and were now firmly convinced of her integrity. Fifty torches flared in their wrought-iron brackets, lighting the rich folds of velvets and satins, making jewels to glow against fair bosoms and gold to glitter on soft, white fingers, causing grotesque shadows to dance on the dim, smoke-enshrouded ceiling.

There was an embrasure to the left of the great fireplace; there the Dauphin, surrounded by courtiers, awaited his guest; he was dressed as those about him. At the farther end of the hall, Clermont, his unvaliant behavior at Rouvray forgotten, sat asprawl on the great gilt throne, joking with La Trémoille and the ladies-in-waiting, calling the most richly-dressed and important-looking of the nobles to stand with deferential mien near the steps of the throne.

They were coming. . . . Word flew from mouth to

mouth. She had been at her prayers when the King's messenger told her that the Dauphin waited to grant her audience. Had she changed into court dress, the ladies asked of the messenger. No, she had risen and come, just as she was; she had not spoken as they rode up the steep, hilly path to the Castle; but once she broke her silence—to a sentry on horseback at the great drawbridge, who had passed a coarse remark and reinforced it by an oath when he heard that it was the Maid who rode through. She had not reproved him for his insult to her maidenhood, however; it was his swearing she took exception to. "You swear by God's Name," she said, "and you so near your death."

The great ladies shivered and begged to know what was delaying the girl; Louis of Bourbon, the Count of Vendome, was conducting her through the maze of buildings; they should be here at any moment, the messenger thought. They *were* here; there were her two squires, Jean of Metz and Poulengy, just coming through the door; and here was Louis of Bourbon ushering her in. That was she—in the grey hose and tunic, with the dark leathern jerkin. That was the Maid.

She stood for a moment blinking in the light of the torches, waiting for her eyes to get used to the change from the dusk outside. So this was the court; and these the courtiers. She who had known brighter radiance and spoken with the nobles of Heaven, stood grave and silent before this battery of staring eyes. A court gentleman stepped forward and preceded her towards the throne. Two ladies-in-waiting giggled audibly; necks craned;

there was another hush; how clever of His Highness to have thought of this little deception.

"That is not the Dauphin," the Maid's country accents rang strange in the great room.

"Clermont!" (and Jean of Metz could have cheered her to the echo) "the King's captain would serve him better by remaining at Orleans with le Bâtard, than by sitting at ease on his throne."

She turned to Louis of Vendome: "Where is the Dauphin?" A noble came from the right, and another from the left; she shook her head. "Why would you mislead me, good people? I came to aid him. And I shall know him though you play a hundred foolish tricks."

Suddenly she saw the man she sought; going towards the fireplace she curtseyed—quite a time it had taken her, practising it for the past two days—and spoke her message: "Noble Dauphin. I am called Jeanne the Maid. The King of Heaven bade me come tell you that you shall receive the sacred oils and the crown of France in the city of Rheims. He sent me to bring help to you and your realm."

"Who sent you?" interrupted La Trémoille, who had come down the room to witness her encounter with Charles.

"The King of Heaven, Who is also King of all the realms of this world; He wills that the English leave France and return to their own land. And He wills that you, Sire," she spoke directly to the Dauphin, "rule this country in fief for Him. And may He give you long life."

A buzz of conversation filled the entire hall. In the

general hubbub, the Count of Clermont slipped outside to fret and fume over his discomfiture; the Archbishop of Rheims also went out. It was twenty years since he had been consecrated Archbishop, and as yet he had neither visited his city nor seen his magnificent cathedral; perhaps it would have been better if he had gone there occasionally, but it was pleasant living at court, moving about from one château of the Dauphin's to another. If the worst came to the worst, he and La Trémoille were not without friends—powerful friends—among the English and the Burgundians; in fact, he had certain provisional arrangements made in case Orleans fell; and it was fairly certain that it would fall. The effrontery of this hoyden from Lorraine, to make arrangements for him—the Archbishop of Rheims—and in his own cathedral, too, was not to be borne. That insufferable Yolande and her *clique* had primed the girl well; and that pious ass, the King's confessor, advising Charles to give her a hearing! The prelate, seething with a rage by no means holy, moved away to his own sumptuous apartments; there he paced to and fro, frowning heavily at the galling remembrance of Jeanne's usurpation of his powers. Arranging a coronation at which he should officiate! The world was indeed topsy-turvy when an illiterate but presumptuous peasant lass could so slight a churchman of his standing.

In a little while La Trémoille entered; easing his great bulk into a window-seat, he beckoned Chartres towards him. When La Trémoille beckoned, the one to whom he beckoned, came—and quickly; even His Grace, the Archbishop of Rheims. In his youth a chamberlain of

Duke John of Burgundy, La Trémoille contrived most of his life to stand with a foot in both camps. At an early stage of his association with the Dauphin's court, he had sized up the indolent, feeble-shanked prince, and noted how favourites ruled him. It was a comparatively easy matter for astute La Trémoille to egg on the stern Breton, de Richemont, then Constable of France, to rid the realm of two particularly obnoxious favourites, and, once safely installed in their shoes, to persuade his doting master to banish to Britanny the austere Constable who had helped the erstwhile chamberlain to prominence. . . . His marriage to the beautiful young widow of one of the murdered favourites had been the most splendid sight the Dauphin's court had seen in these days of exile. Greedy of wealth as of power, treacherous, unscrupulous, a born intriguer, La Trémoille was hated and feared and—consequently—treated with much deference by both friend and foe.

"He gave her a private audience," he announced; "I know not what transpired, but when he returned his countenance seemed changed. He was more sure of himself; whatever these secrets were which she says that she was told to reveal to him, and to him alone, they were pleasant to his ear. I took the precaution of having a fellow posted in an alcove in the chamber used for private audiences, but the Dauphin searched the room before letting her speak and turned out my man."

"What attitude should we adopt towards this impudent wench?"

"For the present we shall not commit ourselves one way or another. In fact, it might be well to dissemble a little, and let all think that we are of the same mind concerning her as is the Dauphin. But work for delay; if Charles seems to be on the point of agreeing to furnish her with the men and arms she craves for to save Orleans, you must step in, as Councillor of France and as the leading churchman at the court, and insist that she first submit to a lengthy examination to decide whether her visions are of Heaven or of Hell. That should make delay long enough for the English to take Orleans; and, if it does get as far as an ecclesiastical enquiry, and if we cannot find sufficient churchmen to get us a majority there, well—there are ways and means of dragging out such proceedings." And, heaving himself out of the window-seat, his shadow a menacing and bloated darkness that reached from floor to ceiling, La Trémoille left as quietly and as quickly as he had come.

The Archbishop stood at the window where his guest had been sitting, staring out over the river. There was a sudden clamour in the courtyard below. Men-at-arms ran towards the moat. Torches and lanterns flamed over the dark waters. Flinging wide the casement, the Archbishop demanded the reason for the commotion. It was a sentry whose horse had taken fright and flung him in the moat. They had just fished out his body. He was drowned. It was the fellow who had sentinelled the drawbridge. The one to whom the Maid had spoken, warning him that death was near for him. The Archbishop closed the window, drawing the heavy curtains to shut out the cold damp air of night, reflecting, as he did so, that there are no casements in the mind, no tapestries to shield the heart from chill forebodings. He had too

much in common with La Trémoille—their mutual in-
terests ran on planes too parallel—for the visit of the
Dauphin's favourite to have caused His Grace undue
perturbation. It was otherwise with this incident in the
courtyard, this sudden, grim fulfilment of the Maid's
prophecy. Whence was she—the girl they called Jeanne
d'Arc—of Heaven or Hell? Who had so swiftly avenged
the insult to her honour? Hardly the powers of evil;
Hell would not champion virtue by attacking the one
who impugned it. The man-at-arms had mocked at the
Maid's virginity; Satan would not harm him for that, nor
for his swearing by God's Holy Name—the act Jeanne
d'Arc had reproved him for. If this sudden death, which
appeared to be a judgment and condemnation, had not
been the work of the devil, it must have been . . . But
the Archbishop could not bear to face the only alterna-
tive explanation. Leaving his apartments, he hastened to
join the courtiers revelling in the banquet hall.

Chapter Five

I F PARIS, with its great university, was the mind of
France, Orleans was the heart. Paris had learning and
science; Orleans had honour and valour. To Paris all
Christendom flocked, lured by the dazzling genius of
French scholars; to Orleans returned all France when
faith needed rekindling and patriotism reanimating. Paris
was where the fickle mobs ran riot, wasting good French
blood, now of this generation, now of that; Orleans was
where a great nation perennially renewed itself, where
its heart throbbed, steady and strong. All the roads of the
world crossed in Paris, bringing travellers from every
nation on earth—from north, south, east and west they
came—to marvel and pass on. All the roads of France
criss-crossed in Orleans and there Frenchmen stood, their
eyes looking out across the plain of Beauce, straining
towards Chartres, their backs to the teeming provinces
of the South, their loyalties flooding over in great surges
like the Loire at a time of high tides.

At Orleans, Attila aimed a death-blow in the fourth century; there he and his Huns were repelled by the good Bishop who later became St. Aignan, patron of the town. And, in the fifteenth century, when England and traitor Burgundy gathered in strength to give France the *coup de grâce,* French fighting men instinctively fell back on Orleans. It had been the last bastion before—in 1429—the besieged town awaited the battle that would either free France or leave her forever in bonds.

The town had been under siege for fully six months. Hearing of the horrors that had befallen the inhabitants of other towns surrendering to Talbot or Salisbury, the fifteen thousand souls who were proud to call themselves citizens of Orleans decided that if they had to die by the hands of the English, they might as well go down fighting. A few might hope to be spared—wealthy and influential burghers like Jacques Boucher and his father-in-law—for the sake of the ransom they would fetch, but plain folk might expect no better treatment than to be sewn in sacks and thrown into the Loire. The knights who had defended Melun—brave fellows who had held out until every horse and dog in that town had been devoured—had they not been trussed and parcelled and pitched into the Seine? And see what had happened in le Mans; the citizenry driven like cattle into the principal square and butchered, every one.

With such foes it availed nothing to surrender meekly; whether a town gave in soon or late, death—and a not very pleasant death at that—was the only prospect ahead. Yet there was always the hope that, by holding out, the impossible might happen; the royalist forces might yet be rallied and come upon the besiegers and rout them. Meanwhile, let the English pay dearly for the privilege they hoped to have eventually—the sacking of Orleans. Every day that they were held at bay put up the price; it cost no mean sum to keep thousands of *Goddams* fed and armed and ever ready.

Good Friday fell on the 25th of March. The coincidence of the great mysteries and feasts of Our Lord and Our Lady, the Incarnation and Redemption, the Annunciation and Compassion, did not go unnoticed; the old rhyme was on all lips:

> *When Our Lord falls in Our Lady's lap*
> *'Twill mean for England great mishap.*

Looking back over the half-year just gone, and remembering all they had endured, the hearts of the people of Orleans beat high with pride. Even if they had to surrender now, soon after Easter, as the soldiers and captains were saying, their names would be remembered forever in France. Aye, far beyond the frontiers of France, wherever fighters met together, wherever the French language—yes, and the English, too—was spoken, the story of Orleans' brave stand and the valour of its citizens would be told and sung.

Men would tell of the fatal day the previous October when Salisbury, with forty captured French towns to his credit, came marching on Orleans, daring to pillage and burn the church of Notre Dame de Clery as his first salute to the beleaguered. What a sight it was to look out along the Loire and see the churches, convents, windmills, hamlets go up in flames one after another, as the English approached nearer and nearer. What feverish preparations went on within the walls, the citizens hardly pausing to ask the watchers on the towers how near the enemy was, or how great were his forces; soon the whole strength of the coming army could be seen from the town. Almost all the *Goddams* were mounted, even the archers (dear God! while some of the French forces were glad to ride cattle if they could come by them!). Behind came the baggage-train, hundreds of carts straggling along in a great file that reached back as far as the eye could see, the lowing of the oxen that drew them plaintive to hear; seated on the loads of provender and arms were the officers' women; the other women camp-followers came along on foot, young French girls most of them, girls from Melun and le Mans . . . girls from forty fallen towns of France. . . .

These girls and their dishonour might be forgotten, but the valiant women of Orleans would never be forgotten—they who had stood on the walls beside their men the day Salisbury stormed the fortress at the end of the bridge. Many a soft arm was burned when pots and pans of red-hot coals, boiling oil and scalding water were poured on the English who attempted to scale the walls; many a fair face was smudged with smoke and sweat—and tears, . . . Alas! Despite such efforts, a few days later the enemy mined the outworks of the fort and it had to be abandoned. The flag of St. George was run up and Salisbury rode by to see the sight, and—blessed be God!—a stray cannon-ball came from a cannon no one remembered firing, and stopped the dread Earl for ever. "A fitting end for a pillager of holy places," said the people, as they crowded their churches, giving thanks for the early removal from the fray of him whose reputation as a commander and a fighter—and a butcher—was second to none.

The very day after the English lost their commander, the French got back theirs. Fresh hope came when Jean, le Bâtard d'Orléans, rode in through the Burgundy Gate, with the reinforcements he had hurriedly grouped together on hearing of the city's plight. Brave, eloquent, hero of a hundred battles, the handsome knight was cheered to the echo as he passed by, some of the bravest captains of France in his company, with almost a thousand archers and Italian men-at-arms marching behind.

"You can't deny blood; whatever his mother may have been, Duke Louis of Orleans lives again in le Bâtard."

"Who was his mother, anyway?"

"Wife of a certain Sieur de Cany, it was said; it's so long ago now; he must be twenty-five."

"Poor Duke Louis! Hard to say which of the two brothers met the worse fate—Louis murdered in his prime, King Charles going mad."

"Charles fared the worse—married to that strumpet, Isabelle of Bavaria. What a one to crown Queen of France! They say that she allowed the court servants to neglect and ill-treat her husband; they let him—the King of France, mark you!—go about filthy and untended as any orphaned village idiot. And when she and Philip of Burgundy—traitor and son of a traitor—signed that treaty with the English in Troyes, she was vile enough to allow it to be recorded therein that there was a doubt about

whether mad Charles was the Dauphin's father or not.
A depraved and shameless wanton, no more fit to be a
mother than she was to be a queen, that's what Isabelle
was. Duke Louis met misfortune, but nothing like as bad
as his poor brother."

"How did Louis' grand wife—she was a princess, too,
wasn't she—how did she take it when they told her of the
base-born son like a cuckoo in the Sieur de Cany's nest?"

"She was a great lady, truly great, Valentina of Milan.
The moment she heard of that child, she sent for him
and had him brought up with her own children. 'He's
son of the first prince in France,' she said, 'and I'll see
that he is brought up as befits one of the blood royal;
and may he inherit not his father's few faults, but his
many graces and virtues.' "

"And when the Duke was murdered, did she still stand
up for le Bâtard?"

"Didn't I tell you that she was a great lady? I saw her
in tears at the court of mad Charles, pleading for justice
for her orphans and herself, and accusing Burgundy of
Louis' murder; her children were with her, all lovely as
she, all weeping for their father; it was le Bâtard she had
by the hand, he was then four. 'This one also should
have been mine,' she said, sadly, 'he was stolen from me.
And of all these orphans none is so well fitted to avenge
my Lord the Duke's death as this dear lad.' She died the
following year, but not without making provision for
young Jean's future. Italian though she was, she foresaw
what Frenchmen could not see, that this Orleans, though
his arms bore the baton-sinister, would prove the noblest
of them all."

Thus the good citizens of Orleans reminisced as they lined the streets to welcome their idolised Commander. Where now were the prophets of woe who had said that he would never return, that he had failed to get reinforcements? Le Bâtard not succour the town whose name he so proudly bore—the town he commanded in the name of the Dauphin!

With his advent, the morale of the besieged stiffened and held firm through that autumn of alarms and anxieties. Everyone became, of necessity, a soldier; swords, hatchets, kitchen knives, scythes, implements pertaining to the various trades, were used for arms; the women and boys had no easy task keeping the molten lead and boiling tallow constantly heated. In November the city fathers, after consultation with the military and ecclesiastical authorities, decided to sacrifice all the churches and convents on the outskirts of the city, fearing that some night the enemy might suddenly occupy these buildings and completely surround the town. Lots had to be cast before anyone in Orleans would set fire to the piles of vine-branches and straw heaped up within the consecrated cloisters and buildings; the unfortunate fellow finally chosen ran with his torch from one sacred edifice to another, praying as he did so that God and Our Lady and the saints might forgive him. The citizens stood by watching their dearest treasures go up in flames. When the Cathedral was set alight, all fell on their knees and apologised to the patron of Orleans, that Bishop who had saved the town in other evil days: "*Messire* St. Aignan, forgive what we do; forsake us not in the time of our need."

Seventeen churches in all were destroyed before Christmas—the work of generations levelled in a few weeks. Denuded of so many of its thirty-five towers, stripped of so many splendid spires, that Christmas, Orleans presented a forlorn sight, surrounded by blackened cinder-strewn wastes, scarred by unsightly ruins and charred walls; and on the little islands in the Loire heaps of corpses made meals for the birds of prey that filled the air with their raucous cries.

But Christmas was truly Christmas in 1428. The fighting ceased in honour of the Prince of Peace. Sir John Talbot—in command since Salisbury's unlamented end—requested le Bâtard to send him musicians for a concert, "fiddles, trumpets and clarionets"; whereupon a goodly company of the best musicians in Orleans was mustered and bidden betake themselves to the great encampment outside the town and there play English carols. The people of Orleans thronged the walls and draw-bridge to listen; right well did the players acquit themselves; the *Goddams* sang with a will; so well they might, replete with the good food which could be smelt by the hungry ones within the walls and on the bridge. However, things were not too bad, seventeen pigs, and eight horses laden with wheat and fat kids having been slipped into the town the previous day; and as the musicians strolled back, each man had a Christmas gift of food beneath his arm, whilst a herald came with them, bearing a dish of figs for the Commander of Orleans. These Christian courtesies exchanged, on the next day the siege was resumed with renewed vigor, the English cannon battering away at the walls, the French *culverins* and *bombardes* retorting in kind.

Near the end of January, a fresh diversion occurred when one day a great clamour and much clashing of arms outside the Regnart Gate brought the garrison rushing to that entrance, the sentinel of which was so beside himself with surprise and joy that he could not tell enquirers what was afoot. A well-known shout from without galvanised the soldiers into action; flinging wide the gate they found La Hire, that doughty Gascon whose prowess in battle was the talk of France, hacking his way—himself and his thirty men-at-arms—into Orleans. Rushing to his aid le Bâtard and his men forgot their hunger for an hour, the very sight of bluff La Hire heartening them to give battle to those few *Goddams* who had attempted to intercept him. A company of English archers, who should have aided their comrades, seemed to have been rendered inert by the shock of seeing the Captain from Gascony back again—when they had thought and hoped him far away. They looked on, mesmerised, as their fellows were routed and La Hire entered Orleans.

A few weeks more and dire disaster struck; that rout which made them the laughing-stock of the *Goddams* on the Saturday before Lent, "Herrings Day," the *Goddams* called it afterwards, remembering the herrings destined for Lenten fare, trodden underfoot by the fighting men. Such a Lent there never was in Orleans. There was fasting and feasting: fasting on the days, and they were many, when no convoy of supplies managed to slip through the open end of the horse-shoe of enemy forts and outposts; feasting on the good days when a herd of cattle, a flock of sheep, pack-horses laden with cooking-oils, wines, or wheat, were rushed in by partisans from the surrounding plains, as well as by the smugglers who lived by running the blockade on besieged towns, and who stipulated that the garrison should make sorties and draw the enemy's attention elsewhere, the while they moved their four-footed and excessively high-priced merchandise into the city.

And now Lent was drawing to its close, and so was the siege. They could hold out no longer. In desperation the city council decided to approach Philip of Burgundy; better the son of the murderer of Duke Louis of Orleans than the English. They proposed to surrender the town to him, and guaranteed that they would pay the expenses the English would be sure to demand, if he would come and take possession of Orleans. Philip was pleased at the prospect of becoming the Lord of the chief city of the Armagnacs, but he reckoned without his English allies. "Is Duke Philip to get the richest spoils of wars waged at the loss of so much good English blood and English gold?" they asked. "We chew the meat for Burgundy to swallow it! With victory in sight he asks us to hand him over Orleans. Not likely! Once Orleans is ours, it's only a matter of months before all France south of the Loire is an English province."

The Duke of Bedford, Regent of France for the child-King, Henry VI of England, was married to Burgundy's sister. He did not approve of his brother-in-law's ambitions and sent him a curt note. "We will take Orleans as soon as we feel like it; and then the expenses we incurred during the siege will be paid, and in full. I do not beat the bushes for another to bag the game." In high dudgeon at this insult from Bedford, Burgundy ordered his troops to withdraw from Orleans. As they marched away, Talbot's soldiers jeered them. "Go, blow your bugles and dulcet pipes all the way back to Burgundy," they cried, "and tell the Duke you aren't worth your keep."

In Orleans hope lay dying; only one slender chance of last-moment relief remained. It was the news of the Maid. The same one about whom rumours had been rife some weeks past; the one La Hire spoke of when he came in January. So strange were the tales told, that le Bâtard sent two messengers to Chinon, where she was said to be, early in March; they should be back any day now. What word would they bring? Was she a human maid at all? Some said that she was an angel with great wings furled about her. Oh, that she would spread her wings and fly to the succour of this most sore-pressed city! Would she come in time? . . . Would she come at all? . . .

The *Goddams* sat in their great camp, with its booths covering a goodly area around Orleans. It was nearing the end now; the French were less impudent; there was no word of that swaggering free-booter, La Hire, no, nor of the handsome Bâtard, this while past. In a few more days Orleans would share the fate that had befallen other proud old cities; the English recalled the early days of the Hundred Years War when Edward, he who in youth was called the Black Prince, took Calais. Good Minot had made a song about it, a song of hunger, the last verses of which ran:

> Our horses that were fair and fat
> Are eaten up each one bidene;
> Have we neither coney nor cat
> That are not eaten and hound keen—
> All are eaten up full clean,
> Is neither left bitch nor whelp.
> That is well on our semblance seen
> And they are fled that should us help.

Some old campaigners could tell the tale of Rouen, which twenty years earlier had stood a six months' siege by Harry of Monmouth; that was the worst and longest siege of the French wars, and the people were in sorer straits than those in Orleans. Harry had tightened the blockade and hardened his heart at the sight of the hapless twelve thousand caught between the city walls and the besieging army. One by one they perished, aged folk and women and children, but the cold heart of the conqueror never relented; he watched twelve thousand helpless and innocent creatures die, between the trenches and the city walls. Some said it was a judgment when he died himself a couple of years later of a mysterious illness, in his thirty-third year; a hard commander to serve under, but one who led his men to certain victory; none of this dalliance that went on here at Orleans. My Lord Suffolk asking le Bâtard for fur to line a robe; Talbot asking for musicians; figs and fruit going in to the French commanders. . . . So the *Goddams* grumbled and waited all through April, cooling their heels, waiting for the siege to be raised.

In Orleans, le Bâtard fumed and swore. This delay was all the doing of that wretch, La Trémoille and His Grace of Rheims; traitors both of them; hawking the Maid off to Poitiers, two days' ride up the Vienne, to have her claims and sayings sifted by learned men, to have her examined by honourable matrons to see if she were human or satyr, maid or trollop. She turned the tables on some of them there, La Hire had said. He had loosed his horse one evening, later on swimming the Loire himself under cover of darkness; a long low whistle brought the horse across and La Hire was away to see if he could hasten the advent of the Maid. The Maid was as impatient of this long delay, of these endless questionings, as were those who waited for her in Orleans. Her impatience sometimes betrayed itself in a certain sauciness that would, in spite of herself, creep into her answers to the endless questions being put to her by the tribunal.

La Hire elbowed his way into the house in Poitiers where they had lodged the Maid and where they had now gathered to question her. He had spoken with the Dauphin and the Archbishop of Rheims earlier that morning, swearing great oaths and cursing roundly the cautious courtiers who had persuaded Charles into sending the Maid to Poitiers—a town abounding in lawyers, dons and theologians. Why not let her ride to Orleans first and then decide whether her Voices came from Heaven or Hell, demanded La Hire. Did they not realise to how desperate a pass things had come in Orleans? Did they not know that the fame of this Maid had reached there and the citizens were waiting and praying for her to come? Even the *Goddams* had heard of her and were in some trepidation at the thought of a witch from Lorraine coming to fight them. Yes, they knew all that, but

Charles thought it better to have the girl examined by men knowledgeable and prudent; La Trémoille had advised such a course.

La Hire spat on the ground and swore still greater oaths, then strode away to see what went on at the Tribunal. Seventeen they said she was; a fine wench for her years; and, by Heaven! the lass had spirit. "So you have come to question me—who knows neither A nor B!" she rallied the grave monks and doctors as they filed into the little room and arranged themselves on the seats facing the wooden bench where she sat. Regnault of Chartres, the Archbishop of Rheims, was presiding. That Carmelite with the Limousin accent asked what language her Voices spoke. "Better French than yours," retaliated the Maid. La Hire, at the doorway, laughed aloud and smote his thigh. My Lord of Rheims would have liked to order him away, but no one in Christendom ordered La Hire. "Dost thou believe in God?" It was the same questioner with the broad accent that bespoke his southern origin.

"More strongly than yourself," rejoined Jeanne. Even those standing in the doorway like La Hire could see that her patience was wearing thin. Asked why God, to Whom all things are possible, did not deliver France without the help of those men-at-arms she so ceaselessly demanded, she replied that if they but gave her the soldiers, God would soon show how He gives victories through human means. Still the Court hesitated. Why, they asked, were they to risk the lives of men on the word of a girl—one scarce more than a child? One demanded a miracle to prove that God really stood behind the Maid; another asked for some sign. "In God's Name!" cried the exasperated girl, "I did not come here to work miracles. Send me to Orleans and then you will see signs and miracles in plenty. Only give me what soldiers you think fitting and I will go raise the siege. That I promise. But to Orleans I will go, whether you give me few or many."

La Hire hung about Poitiers for some days; then he rode back to Orleans, slipping in this time with a line of pack-horses being rushed in through one gate while a sortie was in progress at another. As soon as he could, he told le Bâtard how things were going in Poitiers. He told of the letter the Maid had sent during Holy Week to no less than Bedford himself; the notary who took it down as she spoke it had read his copy of it for La Hire. "You who *call yourselves* Regent and Lieutenants of France," she had begun; she had demanded that they yield to her the keys of all the conquered French towns. She gave them a chance of making peace before she came to fight them—provided they did justice and restored what they had seized. She had also addressed herself to the men fighting under these English Lords and bade them be off to their own land while they might. La Hire could not remember the rest of the letter very well, except that she had told them that if they failed to hearken to her warning, they would soon see who had the better right from God to be in France, the French or the English.

"How can they see soon if she does not come?" asked le Bâtard. "Did you tell them how it was with us here?"

"That I did. But you know the ways of courtiers like La Trémoille and Chartres the Archbishop, and learned men like those on the Council in Poitiers. They are more concerned with the turn an argument takes than with the hunger in Orleans."

From hints he had picked up here and there, he had concluded that La Trémoille and the Archbishop were behind this delay and wanted Orleans to fall to Bedford. The Maid, however, had a goodly following of influential friends; La Hire had spoken with them and urged that the proceedings be hastened. The young Duke of Alençon was all for supporting Jeanne and riding at once for Orleans; the Queen of Sicily was another who was working night and day to forward the march on Orleans; and that good fighter, d'Aulon, La Hire had been speaking to him and to two squires from Vaucouleurs who had escorted her to Chinon.

"Did you have speech with the Maid herself?" La Hire was asked.

"Just once. She could not have known me as I was but newly arrived in Poitiers. I was riding past where they have lodged her—the Hôtel de la Rose, in the centre of the town—when this stripling of a page-boy (as I thought) came and halted me and laid a hand on my bridle-rein. 'Etienne de Vignolles,' she said, and how she knew my name I cannot tell, for well you know that it is a name I have almost forgotten myself, La Hire being the only name I go by this twenty years. And then, as if she knew my thoughts, she went on: 'Captain La Hire, soon we will ride together and save France. This delay in Poitiers is not of my making; but despite this hindrance I shall be in Orleans ere April is out, and after Our Lord's Ascension the siege shall be raised.'" La Hire, grim campaigner that he was, paused to see if le Bâtard was inclined to scoff at his story.

"It's nigh mid-April now," sighed the Commander. He would have liked to believe La Hire fully, but these fair words of the Maid seemed almost impossible of fulfilment.

"I ride back again tonight," said the other. "The verdict of the Court may be given this evening. Yolande of Sicily is certain of that, and I know that she has not been idle in bringing matters to a head."

"For God's sake, get them to do something or we'll be but skeletons by the time relief comes. It's nothing but hope in the Maid that's keeping half the townspeople alive so long. God knows, their faith in her—and now, your word from her—make me believe in her certain victory, although the odds are so heavily against us."

Greatly elated that his report had been believed, La Hire rode boldly past the enemy outposts, shouting his war-cry *"Montjoie St. Denis!"* as he galloped. Three knights were soon to saddle and hot in pursuit, from the bridge of Orleans up the heights of Olivet, two miles beyond the town; on and on to Clery, where the blackened walls of the College and Church of Notre Dame showed strange in the moonlight. Somewhere between that and Meung they lost him and returned, chagrined, to the camp, by which time La Hire was riding hell-for-leather over the lone wastes of the Sologne, the misery in Orleans spurring him on, the face of Jeanne the Maid the star towards which he rode.

How often he covered that journey in the next two weeks! For, to his amaze and that of all who knew of the machinations of La Trémoille and My Lord of Rheims, opposition vanished, the Commission reported in favour of the Maid, and the court, the loyalist towns in Touraine, and such fighting forces and captains as could be rallied thereabouts were in a very ferment of excitement and enthusiasm. Once he was back to tell not only le Bâtard, but the expectant burghers and garrison of Orleans, of how the Maid was in Tours, that most prosperous of French loyalist centres, where the armourers were—by special order of the Dauphin—making a complete harness for her: helmet, cuirass in four parts, with epaulets, armlets, elbow-shields, shields for the forearms, gauntlets, knee-protectors, greaves and shoes. She had been given a household of her own, like any knight: a steward, two heralds, a bodyguard, and a page, as well as the two squires who had escorted her from Vaucouleurs and who never left her side, and an Augustinian friar named Jean Pasquerel for her confessor. Again he was over the walls at midnight telling of how she had refused the sword made for her, bidding them go search for a sword which her Voices had told her was buried beneath the altar in the church of St. Catherine of Fierbois. La Hire had been there when they dug and found, as she had predicted, a sword engraved with five crosses in honour of Our Lord's five glorious Wounds.

The English tightened the blockade. Feverishly they built three bastions commanding the river from east and west. They, too, had heard that the Maid was coming. The Commander had received her arrogant letter sent just after Easter; the camp-women brought in rumour after rumour; many a good English yeoman crossed himself and wished to God he had never left his native heath to follow the fortunes of war. If it were war, one would not mind. Sitting outside a town for over half a year had been bad enough, but being asked to stand up and fight a foul witch coming armed with the might of Hell, accompanied by her paramours, the fiends—this was more than flesh and blood could endure. Daily the *Goddams* grew more uneasy; they were sorry now that they had let the men of Burgundy go.

But at last the Maid was on the march. On the 25th of April she rode from Tours to Blois; the river was running high, so she went by the south bank, the Archbishop of Rheims and the Sieur de Goucourt on her either side, a sizeable and enthusiastic army tramping behind. Past the castles of Amboise and Chaumont, on to La Beauce, skirting great forests, they travelled, until finally, after riding thirty odd miles, they sighted Blois where it rose steeply on the northern bank of the river. Crossing the humped bridge they found every street and square a mass of cattle, sheep and swine; the Queen of Sicily, who owned Tours, had rounded up great convoys of merchandise and sent them on ahead of the army. Wagons laden with grain, arms and ammunition rumbled along the narrow lanes. And French captains and nobles, suddenly galvanised into action, had ridden to meet her whom all now hailed as the saviour of France, bringing with them armed bands. In all there were over ten thousand assembled in Blois, all proud to march behind the beautiful banner of white buckram fringed with silk, when Jeanne carried it to the Church of St. Sauveur to have it blessed. St. Margaret and St. Catherine had directed her concerning this standard; on one side Our Lord, attended by two angels, blessed the lily of France; on the reverse side Our Lady looked on a shield which bore the French arms; the white ground was sewn with golden *fleur-de-lis*. It was a noble banner to follow and could be seen from afar; those riding in front could also see the two small pennons, one showing the Annunciation, and one—the Maid's private pennon—bearing a white dove on a blue field.

For the next two days Jeanne was busy among the soldiers quartered in and near Blois. She had heard of how low the morale and character of the French army had sunk, but it needed the testimony of her own eyes and ears to realise fully the dissoluteness of the men, the cruelty of the captains, the meanness of those responsible for paying and feeding the forces. As she moved hither and thither, foul and blasphemous language, undreamt of in the Lorraine valley of her childhood, smote her ears; again and again she had to avert her eyes from scenes of drunkenness, lewdness and violence. Innocent but not ignorant, she grieved in her heart that God was so flagrantly set at naught. Up and down the streets and squares she strode, praying without words, wondering what to do, for lead this mob of drunkards and blasphemers and prostitutes she would not—not for a hundred Orleans!

Here and there she was halted by one or other of the great generals who had ridden to meet her. The Duke of Alençon, her ally and her friend since the day he had turned back from his quail-hunt to rally to her aid; La Hire, his lips hot with curses; that strange, deathly-pale

Maréchal with the coal-black hair and stony blue eyes, Gilles de Rais; her squire, d'Aulon—"the most honest man in France."

"Friar Pasquerel," she called, seeing her chaplain a little way from her in the crowd, "I know now why our arms have suffered such reverses in the field. All the afternoon I have gone about." She indicated the scenes on either side. "How can victory come while our army offends God so openly?"

"What would you do, child?"

"My Voices spoke, even as I walked through the camp. They bade me tell the captains assemble all."

"And you will speak?"

"Not this time, nor of this matter; it is you who must speak, not I."

"But, Maid, they'll obey one word from you sooner than a sermon from me. Besides, why should I, a poor friar, speak to the armies of France when there are great churchmen in the camp? His Grace of Rheims, now——"

"Would there were fewer like him on the side of France, and more true priests. No. The Voices said that you were to preach penitence to the soldiers—here and now. Stay by this tree and I will give orders to rally all who would march on Orleans."

Within a little while, a motley congregation faced the Augustinian. Here and there the captains shoved to and fro, bawling commands at the men-at-arms, archers, knights and squires who jostled one another as they surged about the preacher; the women stood on the out-skirts of the crowd, curious to know what was afoot. The friar raised the crucifix. The murmuring ceased.

"The Maid bids me say," began Pasquerel, "that she will not ride at the head of an army of blasphemers and foul-mouthed fellows. Nor need those who prepare by drinking and wenching and brawling for a battle wherein they may lose their lives, hope to follow her to Orleans. If you believe that she is the one whom God has sent to succour France in the hour of need, you must do as she says. Who wishes to share in her victory at Orleans?"

Thousands of voices thundered the reply: "To Orleans! To Orleans and to victory!"

"Tomorrow the Maid marches on Orleans. Tonight she does not order so long a march, but she commands you to follow her a little way. At sun-down she comes to be shriven; those who will march tomorrow must set their souls right tonight. At dawn there will be Mass, where the Maid and her entire army will receive Our Lord, before setting forth."

The women in the background made shrill protest; the soldiery muttered; the captains avoided one another's eyes, each loath to take the initiative and reply to the friar. La Hire was ill at ease; when coming up between the fields of lupin and bean, to know why the trumpets were rallying the men, he had seen the Maid alone in the great tent they had rigged for her a little apart from the camp. She had been praying, praying in a way that La Hire respected if he did not practise. This is what she had been praying for—he was sure of it; for the captains and maréchals, for rascals like Poton and de Rais, for himself—La Hire, the terror of half of France. By the Lord, La Hire would show them all that if not a man of them had the courage to confess, he had, the litany of

whose misdemeanours and crimes was a byword amongst
his friends and a cause of awe and scandal to his foes. He
was guilty of the worst sins in France, but the Maid had
asked her followers to come and be shriven. La Hire
stepped forward, taking his stand beside Pasquerel and
facing the crowd.

"I ride with the Maid tomorrow," he said, "so I do as
she says. Friar, make ready for shriving La Hire; his
story will be long and grievous, I promise you. Who else
wants to ride with the Maid—and me?"

"I come, too, La Hire!" cried the Duke of Alençon.
"And I'll be shriven ere sunset."

"So will I," shouted Saintrailles and d'Aulon simul-
taneously.

"And I." "And I," called Jean of Metz and Poulengy,
pushing in from the centre of the crowd. The cry
"And I" passed from lip to lip.

"Go, each to his own company, and I will fetch the
priests and send them about through the camp, so that all
can confess before midnight. As for the women: those
who brought wives, send them home; the other women
must also be sent away. It is an order from the Maid."

As Friar Pasquerel expected, the men began to grumble
audibly. It was La Hire who again stepped into the
breach. "Better lose the camp-women than have the
Maid sent by God forsake us. If she's to lead us to
Orleans, her orders must be obeyed. . . . Friar! Art
ready to listen to La Hire? Thou'lt find that there's no
sin to which fighting-men are prone but he has committed—not once but many times over. . . . But, wenches
or wines, be they the finest in all France, won't tempt

me to abandon Orleans; La Hire will be ready for war in the morning, all armoured *cap-à-pie*, soul and body, though no one should ride save the Maid and himself."

A great roar of cheering went up. La Hire knelt and made ready to confess his sins. The handsome Duke d'Alençon uncovered and stood a little apart from where the friar awaited La Hire. One by one the captains followed suit. Priests and monks, hastily summoned from the town, were slipping their stoles over their heads, and seating themselves here and there in sequestered spots, waiting for the men to approach. In a short time a hush fell upon the great encampment, as thousands of Frenchmen made ready for Orleans.

Beyond the camp proper, where the women had gathered in little groups to discuss their imminent dismissal, there was consternation. Some wept, some scolded, others cursed the Maid, La Hire and the whole army. When it was almost sunset, Jeanne emerged from her tent and came to the women. She asked them to go. To go for the sake of France. At first there was no response; hostile, mutinous looks said better than words: "What do we care for France? Who cares for us? Does France— or England—or Burgundy? What is France to us or what are we to France?" Looking into those unfriendly eyes, Jeanne remembered the girl from St. Germain whom her father had spoken of only last autumn. . . . That afternoon seemed a life-time ago, now. . . . She did not know what to say to these women, nor could she think of any appeal that might move them to do as she had requested. So she stood and prayed silently, standing tall and austere-looking in her armour. Here and there in the

crowd there were those who, as they looked into the
clear grey eyes of the Maid, remembered quiet valleys
and green hill-tops; verdant woods and wind-swept
moors; little towns with spires climbing into the skies.
There were those, ignorant of the Scriptures, whose
hearts were already echoing the cry, "I will arise and go
to my Father." One by one they agreed to go. Raddled
women with bloodshot eyes and scarred faces pulled
their tawdry, tattered clouts closer about them, shrugged
their shoulders, and moved away. Girls, scarcely as old
as the Maid herself, their boldness and bravado suddenly
fallen from them, mutely acknowledging the great compassion they read in Jeanne's eyes, gathered their poor
belongings and vanished into the dusk, some in little
groups, others alone, silent, as they retraced those first
and most difficult steps of the road back.

Only three held out and flatly refused to go; laughing
shrilly, they roundly abused this Maid from God-only-
knew-where who interfered with other folks' lives in
such uncalled-for fashion. Who was she anyway? Or
who knew anything of her until recently? If the truth
were known she was probably no better than themselves—the camp-woman of one of the captains, maybe,
or of the great Duke d'Alençon, or the Dauphin himself.
Ha! That taunt stung. She had stepped back into her
tent. Why, as yet the English had not even set eyes on
her, but they had a name for her; already they were calling her "The Harlot of the Armagnacs," "The Witch of
Lorraine." She fooled the French, but she hadn't fooled
the English. . . . "Harlot!" "Witch!" "Cow-herd from
Lorraine!" they shouted mockingly, their raucous voices

rasping on the quiet evening air. Ho! Her page was
fetching her horse; she had a mind to ride out of earshot,
no doubt; she could not abide her rightful names.
" 'Maid,' indeed!" "Witch!" "Harlot!"

The Maid came running from her tent and sprang into
the saddle; her page stepped nimbly aside, ducking as
the sword found at Fierbois flashed from its scabbard,
watching wide-eyed as Jeanne rode straight at the camp-
women, her great weapon unsheathed and at the ready.
Without waiting to collect anything that was theirs, the
three fled from the camp, their already bedraggled
hennins askew upon their heads, their only aim in life to
get away before they were run through by this sword,
the flat of which was being used to whack their shoulders. . . . What a she-demon! . . . Some minutes later,
safe on the far side of the town, sure that their pursuer
had gone back to the camp, they rested, congratulating
themselves on their wonderful escape from the Witch.
"Her horse's eyes and hooves flashed sparks," declared
one of the trio as she panted for breath, "perhaps he is
the Witch's familiar spirit."

Back in the camp, the night-air blew in and out among
the tents cleansing, reviving, refreshing. The murmured
"Ego te absolvo" of the priests droned here and there in
the darkness. And in the souls of many men the winds
of Heaven cleansed, revived and refreshed, while the
Paraclete, the Great Captain, saw His bivouacs pitched
and His beacons lit. . . .

In the tent of the Maid, her brothers, Pierre and Jean,
faced their sister. They had ridden from Domrémy to
join her army, they told her. Everyone spoke of her as

the saviour of France. Their mother had sent this ring. She had sent no message, but on Good Friday last, the Feast of the Annunciation, she had made Jacquemin go on pilgrimage with her to the shrine of the Black Virgin, at Le Puy. Their father had sent word that when the war was won he would be first to come join his famous daughter in her hour of victory, if only to make sure that success would not turn her head. Pierre and Jean said that it was foolish staying at home on the farm; Jacquemin could have the farm and welcome; they knew that Jeanne would see to it that her brothers—brothers of the Maid of France—would be placed in positions of honour in her army.

"Speak to me tomorrow," Jeanne told them. "Tonight go, make your confession like the rest of the French army. I will send the page with you to get you food and wine after your journey."

"She didn't seem so pleased to see us," Jean remarked to his brother, as they followed the page.

"What matter?" Pierre replied. "We are here, and we are her brothers. That should suffice to establish us high-up in the French army."

The Maid, alone in her tent, turned the little ring upon her finger. It bore a cross and there were words engraved on it. In the morning the Friar, or one of the captains who could read, would tell her what the words were. She was sorry her brothers had come, though she was glad of news from home. Her mother had sent no spoken message; nothing but this ring. . . . She wished she could speak with her mother now; her mother knew she had never done anything wrong. Yet camp-women had called her witch and harlot. At the memory of the two names they had flung at her, she flushed and hot tears stung her eyes; how her mother would grieve if she knew the names her Jeanne had been called. A torch flickered outside the tent. It was the page, returning. She could not wait until morning to know what was engraved on the ring Isabel d'Arc had sent.

"Can you read?" she asked him.

"A little," he replied.

"Can you read the inscription on this ring?" she asked, holding the ring close to the torch he held.

"It's easy to read that," he said, "just *Jhesus* and *Maria*. The two Names."

Chapter Six

A SHARP WIND had blown all day on Thursday, April 28th, and in the afternoon the slanting, pitiless rain that comes from the east, beat more and more heavily, until in the evening thick sheets of rain driving down from Olivet obscured the landscape, and the men in the little boat being rowed warily up-river could hardly see fifty yards ahead. It was heavy going, pulling against the current and against the gusts of wind, but the boatmen did not mind the exertion, they were rowing the noble Bâtard out to welcome the Maid. They listened enthralled, as La Hire told the Commander of Orleans of the journey from Blois.

On Wednesday morning, after Mass at which the whole army had received the Body of Our Lord, they marched across the bridge, singing *"Veni, Creator Spiritus."* Priests with banners, bare-foot friars, and great churchmen on richly-caparisoned mules; then the Maid in her white armour, her squire d'Aulon bearing her standard, and a great array of nobles, knights, squires and captains; La Hire could see them again, marching in the early dawn. There was Alençon, Duke of the blood royal, half-uncle to le Bâtard himself, a brave soldier and a good Frenchman; only twenty-three, he had made no small sacrifice, in an age when his class were accustomed to put self first and country a bad second, in leaving his lovely young Duchess, his château and his quail-hunting, to rally to the banner of a poor peasant girl. There was Poton de Saintrailles, a reckless cavalry leader, who had fought side by side with La Hire in so many battles—he it was who had the brilliant idea of negotiating with Philip of Burgundy some months agone, thus causing a temporary estrangement between the leaders of the enemy forces. La Hire himself had ridden next the Maid—no need to dwell on his reputation or lack of it, the Gascon grimly reflected; people called him "cut-throat" and "desperado"; the tales of his crimes and cruelties were legend already, so fast and far had the rumours about him spread; not only in his native Gascony was he known, but throughout the length and breadth of France. Behind rode the Maid's two brothers, just arrived to join her forces; and the pages of her household; the two squires who had escorted her from Vaucouleurs to Chinon were also in her company. The three thousand archers and men-at-arms that trudged along behind were headed by the marshals of France, de Boussac, Sainte-Sévère, and that strange young Gilles de Rais in most resplendent armour, wrought with his bearings.

"As fastidious as he's wealthy," observed le Bâtard.

"Rumours say that his craving for knowledge is so urgent that it has led him into strange paths; paths where no man may safely walk," said La Hire.

"He has a library of rare books surpassing even that of the Duc de Berry."

"Yes. When only in his 'teens, he had his players and mummers performing mystery plays in his châteaux. Not that that in itself is anything against the young Maréchal, but gossip says that he's the rotten limb on the Montmorency-Craon tree—and a good tree that was in its day. One that France had reason to be proud of."

"Sorcery?"

"So they say. Sorcery and the kind of inhuman crimes that go with it. It's well he's in the company of the Maid; if anyone can save him she can."

"How large is the convoy, did you say?" The boatmen listened avidly for the reply.

"Six hundred wagons of food and ammunitions, all drawn by fine fatted oxen; behind them four hundred head of cattle; further behind flocks of sheep and great herds of swine."

"Came you by the oak forest of Boulogne?"

"Yes. The swineherds had some ado to keep the swine from running into the forest. On by Chambord Castle and St. Dyé village to St. Laurent des Eaux, where we encamped in the fields last night. The Maid did what no one in the whole army did—slept in her armour. She was very bruised and weary on arising—I heard her tell her brothers. This morning we cut away from the Loire bank, keeping out of sight of the English garrisons at Beaugency and Meung; we came through fields of asparagus and wheat and bean, and past promising vine-yards, then——"

"And did not the English commanders in Beaugency and Meung set out to harry the convoy? With such rich booty to be taken!"

"No. Though their scouts had seen us and they knew our route."

"Sire, we are close up against Notre Dame de Clery," interjected one of the boatmen. The rain lashed their faces as they peered ahead. The lowing of many cattle and the bleating of sheep could be heard, but as yet nothing could be discerned.

"Pull to the bank," ordered le Bâtard. Scrambling on to the slithery grass, he quickly strode towards the long village street of Clery, followed by La Hire.

"Sire," called the latter, "I warn you that the Maid may not receive you well. She thinks the captains have tricked her, bringing her along the south bank of the river, while the enemy and the besieged city are on the north bank. She is angry."

"I come to welcome her to Orleans. Here we are. There's Alençon and Saintrailles. Where is she?"

She was standing gazing at the river, the rain running down her white armour, her head-piece pulled over her forehead. She looked very angry. She *was* very angry—and tired; aching from head to foot with this constraining steel that clothed her. La Hire came to present le Bâtard, but Jeanne spoke first.

"Are you the Commander—le Bâtard d'Orléans?"

"Yes. And I rejoice that you have come."

"Is it you who advised them to bring me by the wrong

side of the river, instead of sending me direct to Talbot and his English?"

"I, and commanders wiser than I, advised such a course, believing it best for success and safety."

"In God's Name! Our Lord gives better and safer counsel! You would deceive me, but it is you yourselves who are deceived." And her glance swept the ring of captains who had gathered about them. "I bring you the finest aid that ever came to captain or city—the help of the King of Heaven. Though He gives it, not for my sake, but because St. Louis and St. Charlemagne have besought him to take pity on the city of Orleans; it is bad enough that the English should hold the Duke of Orleans captive for so long; God will not suffer that the enemy hold both the Duke and his town."

All around were silent. Who had ever heard a prince of the blood berated so roundly by a peasant girl? And without the former either taking offense or resorting to swift and dire punishment! But le Bâtard was understanding. La Hire had told him that the Maid had not yet broken her fast that day, that her armour hurt her. Her hatred of deception was akin to his own, though really he had not meant to deceive the Maid. He had thought that she knew the captains were taking her by the south bank. It was a muddle, he agreed, looking at the vast train of supplies still coming into Clery. And with the cross currents and the strong wind blowing hard as ever down the river, it would be well-nigh impossible to bring the barges and sailing boats up from Orleans, load them with supplies and get them safely back to the town; by Heaven, the girl's plan had been better than that of himself and his captains. He did not wonder that she was angry. He could not know that, being little more than a child, she had been perilously near to tears and that her anger only served as a cloak.

La Hire was speaking earnestly, explaining the position to Jeanne. In control of herself again, and heartily ashamed of her ungracious and curt reception of le Bâtard, she tried to make amends. She smiled at him: "Wait a little. Have patience. The wind will change soon. All will be well."

And, as she spoke, there came a lull in the rain, and the blustering east wind veered to south-east, to south, to south-west, and to west. They stared at the clouds, now scurrying back whence they had come, they noted the branches of the trees, hardly daring to believe what their senses told them. No one spoke but La Hire.

"By—by—by my baton, the wind *has* changed!"

"Since when did you begin swearing by your baton, La Hire?" laughed de Saintrailles.

"Since he confessed last night," said Alençon.

"Since he promised me," said the Maid, smiling.

Le Bâtard had already gone aside, sending orders to Orleans to have the barges put out at once and make, not for Clery, but Chécy, a point some miles farther up-river; at the same time he ordered the herdsmen and wagoners to turn back to Chécy. The English would hear that the supplies were turning back and conclude that the relieving forces were retreating.

When the Commander returned, the captains still stood with the Maid. He spoke to Jeanne.

"Enter Orleans with me, Maid, tonight. The citizens long sorely to see you."

"But these captains tell me that the army must march back again to Blois in order to come down by the north bank; and even now we are arranging to turn and march tonight. I cannot leave the army. If I let them go alone, they may not all march back on the opposite bank. They may not come back as I brought them—good men, all penitent and confessed. Perhaps another trick will be played on me and these captains may not bring back my army——" She looked uncertainly at the maréchals and knights.

"For the welfare of the King, I beg of you, my lords, to give the army safe conduct to Blois and back, and allow the Maid to enter Orleans at once." Le Bâtard could not contemplate entering his city again without bringing her who was to save it.

But none of the captains wanted to lead the soldiers back the thirty odd miles and up the northern bank; all wished to be in the Maid's train, entering Orleans; and it was obvious that Jeanne herself wanted to be with the men-at-arms. La Hire suggested that her chaplain, Pasquerel, and the company of priests who had marched at the head of the army on the way to Orleans, should be entrusted with the task of accompanying the army on the return to Blois and the march along the northern bank of the Loire. Jeanne could trust Friar Pasquerel to look after the troops. De Boussac and La Hire, with a company of two hundred lances, would remain and cross in the boats with Jeanne and the Commander of Orleans. After some argument and a little persuasion, all agreed to this course. Pasquerel was summoned and received orders from the Maid to bring the entire army back to her as she gave it to him—all good men, penitent and shriven.

Immediately, preparations began for the march back to Blois; each captain went to his company. Here and there fires had been lit, despite the swampy condition of the ground and the greenness of the branches used for firewood; huge copper pots steamed appetisingly; and the soldiers dried their wet garments as well as they could. The captains gave orders: each man was to get a good hot meal and take a few hours' sleep; at midnight they would begin the march back to Blois. But Friar Pasquerel, coming up, brought a new order from the Maid. The men were to get a full night's rest before starting their double journey; at dawn they were to hear Mass, as they did on the previous days when she was with them, and then begin the march back. The English scouts would bring word that the French army had retreated without even giving battle, and Talbot would be lulled into a false security.

Meanwhile, Jeanne with her brothers crossed the Loire, La Hire, de Boussac, le Bâtard d'Orléans and two hundred lances forming her retinue. It was late and two knights from the Orleans garrison were waiting to warn them that the English were keeping a keen watch. Better not enter the town, the Commander decided; on the morrow, news of the army's retreat would have reached Talbot and vigilance would be relaxed. For tonight the Maid would be lodged in the house of Guy de Cailly, a rich burgher of the little town of Chécy on the farther bank.

Thus it came about that one man, of all the people of France, shared in one of the Maid's visions. Having arranged for the lodging of all these late-coming guests, some in his own mansion, some in the village, the *seigneur* of Cailly prepared to retire. On his way up the wide staircase, he paused outside the fine chamber that had been given to the Maid. Someone was speaking with her. She was speaking also, in low, urgent tones. But who could it be? All the Cailly household, save the master, were abed. And La Hire, de Boussac and the Commander of Orleans were in the west wing—de Cailly had just left them there. Who would blame the *seigneur* of Cailly for dousing his own light and drawing aside the arras that curtained the entrance to that room illumined with a light brighter than all the lamps of earth? The best room with its beautiful furnishings seemed but a poor place for the splendid beings whose brightness hurt his poor human eyes, whose voices were too piercingly sweet for his ears. Suddenly he was unable either to listen or look. There were three of them, all in azure and silver raiment, speaking earnestly with the Maid, who knelt before them. . . . That was all Guy de Cailly knew until morning when his page found him lying, as it were, asleep on the staircase. Thinking that his master had constituted himself bodyguard to the famous guest, the page thought nothing of the incident. But the *seigneur* of Cailly hastened to tell the three captains of his experiences; to his amazement, none of the three seemed to doubt his word. They had long since accepted the Maid as one whose counsel was of Heaven.

Friday dragged by, slowly. The morning and forenoon

were hours of feverish activity for le Bâtard and La Hire as they arranged for the flotilla of barges to be loaded with supplies, cattle, sheep, swine and ammunition. Then the word was given to let the boats drift down-stream, keeping close to the sally and poplar trees that fringed the island where the English had a fort; the fort was at the farther side of that island, and La Hire would arrange for a sortie there just at the time when the boats passed. Le Bâtard would lead a similar attack from Orleans on the other English forts; while de Boussac and the two hundred lances could keep an eye on the flotilla and harry any enemy forces that might come in their way.

The Maid had to wait at Chécy. The better to curb her impatience, she spent the day in prayer, thanking God for her safe journey, for the relief she had been enabled to bring, and which was even now pouring in through the gates of Orleans. She fasted all that day. At last the Commander rode back, magnificently accoutred, his great gilt gauntlets shining in the evening sun. He had come to conduct the Maid to his city—henceforth and forever hers.

"There is high excitement in Orleans," he told her, "already there are watchers on the walls and on the towers, ready to give word of your approach."

"How many souls in your city, Bâtard?"

"About seventeen thousand, counting the soldiers of the garrison and those who rallied to our defence."

"What trades do they follow, in times of peace—all these thousands?"

"Why, there are goldsmiths and painters and statue-makers; and chandlers and masons and wood-workers, as there are in other cities. And clerics and scholars, churchmen and physicians; and, like all other towns, we have more than our share of rogues and idlers and thieves. But the back-bone of Orleans is its good burghers, its merchants, and the goodly number of honest citizens who loved their city so well that there was no sacrifice too great—and they were called upon in the last half-year to forego much that makes life bearable—nothing mattered save that they hold out for the Dauphin and for you, Maid."

"When do we ride into Orleans?"

"When the first stars shine. It were well to ride past the English posts in the half-light; I have had a white charger brought for you. Your page can ride ahead on the black, carrying your casque on a cushion. The *seigneur* of Cailly is himself seeing to it that your mount will be fittingly caparisoned."

"My standard—and my pennon of the Annunciation! They will be carried with us?"

"Yes. I will see if all is in readiness. Make ready, Maid, for Orleans!"

The stars called to one another. A white mist lay along the Loire; from fields without the walls came sounds barely distinguishable in silent, waiting Orleans—the bark of a dog, the fretful lowing of a calf parted from the cow, the apprehensive bleating of sheep sensing the sheep-dog turned killer; the vixen's long-drawn cry came from some near-by copse. Within the walls of Orleans there was suppressed excitement; crowds hurried to one gate, hearing that she was coming in there; then to another gate, as rumour changed.

Le Bâtard had said that he would ride when the first stars were up. There were many stars now. And soon in the streets of Orleans a thousand torches and flambeaux would blaze forth to light the way of the Maid. Not a window, not a balcony, but was hung with draperies—tapestry and cloth-of-gold in the case of the rich, gay cloths and bed-spreads in the narrow streets of the poor. Lilac and cherry and pear branches, laden with fragrant blossom, hung over the unsightly ruins of the towers and buildings razed to the ground last November. Ribbons fluttered in every hand, the colours of the house of Orleans, vermillion red and nettle green. Not a child went early to bed that night; not a monk or nun but stood at the entrances to their monasteries and enclo-sures, waiting for a glimpse of the one God had sent to succour Orleans. At last the watchmen at the Bourgogne Gate cried out: "Here they come! The Maid is at the Bourgogne Gate!" And a mighty cheer went up from every wall and street and lane-way, as the citizens thronged to the gate in the eastern wall. . . . And in the silent, listening English encampment, men crossed them-selves and shivered for very fear. . . . The Witch had come. . . . The dread Witch of Lorraine.

Le Bâtard d'Orléans rode on the left of the Maid, his heart high with pride in his city and its people—the best patriots in all France! He would not exchange Orleans, despite its shattered churches, its ruined towers, its menaced, encircled walls, for any city in Christendom; not for all the wealthy towns of Flanders; nor for the cities of Lombardy and Milan, with their priceless heritage of architecture, sculpture and painting; not even for lovely Paris itself. Rumour had said that the Dauphin, Charles, spoke of making him, le Bâtard d'Orléans, Count of Dunois. Charles could keep his titles. Base-born le Bâtard had been; that was not of his doing; what *was* of his doing was the fact that he had tried, all his life, to overcome that handicap of birth by living as became one in whose veins the royal blood of Orleans flowed; to live as befitted the grandson of Charles the Wise, that most noble monarch, the third and the greatest King of the Valois dynasty. He wished for no title save that which France gave him—le Bâtard d'Orléans. Glancing at his companion, he saw that she was weeping, overcome by the tumultuous reception. The crowds pressed in upon the Maid, the children running to and fro beneath the horses' bellies, that they might seize her stirrup or the points of her boots to caress and kiss; maidens young as Jeanne herself, threw flowers in the air; everyone called to her, cheered for her, prayed and wept as she passed along to the church of La Croix. At one point a torch was held so near, its bearer anxious to behold the face of the Liberatrix, that her pennant took fire, but before La Hire or le Bâtard could turn to help, she herself had struck spurs into her mount, turning with a skill a knight might envy and adroitly extinguished the flame with her mailed fist. In the church of La Croix, packed to the doors, prayers were said and a *Te Deum* sung. It was after ten o'clock before Jeanne was at last at her lodgings, the house of Jacques Boucher, Treasurer to the Duke of Orleans.

Madame Boucher had a fine supper prepared; now that the siege had been, in part, lifted, one could again set a fit repast before distinguished guests. The Commander had to get back to the garrison to see how things were there. "Make her eat well," he told the host and hostess. "She has not broken her fast today."

But though Madame Boucher lamented and Jacques cajoled, the Maid would have nothing but a little wine, diluted with water, and a few soppets of bread. She admitted that she was weary and would be glad to retire. As was customary in the case of highly-honoured guests, Madame invited Jeanne to share a bed-chamber with herself and her little daughter, Charlotte. Jeanne and Charlotte would share the best bed. All the way up the staircase, Charlotte trailed behind, fascinated by the spurs and the shining armour.

"Can I fetch you anything? Can I do anything for you?" Madame Boucher asked, solicitously, the moment they were in the bed-chamber.

"Oh, Madame! Unharness me, if you can. It is not easy raiment for a woman to wear—armour."

The good woman exclaimed aloud with compassion as she saw the weals and bruises that showed beneath the cuirass and corselet, epaulets and armlets. She bade Charlotte fetch warm water, unguents and clean strips of old linen; in the early morning she herself would gather herbs in the herb-garden and bind cooling bandages on those places where the armour chafed. Stupid armourers, not to realise how soft a girl's body was, compared to a man's! She would have Jacques take that suit of mail to the Duke's armoury first thing tomorrow and have adjustments made. Gratefully, Jeanne yielded herself to Madame Boucher's kindly and comforting hands. It was good to be among women-folk again. The capable fingers massaged, bathed and bandaged far into the night. But the Maid, too weary and exhausted to heed her ministrations, slept as soundly as did the nine-year-old Charlotte, who had carefully withdrawn to the other side of the great bed.

.   .   .   .   .

At the first glimmer of dawn on the eve of Ascension Thursday, the Maid and La Hire, at the head of five hundred men, set out to meet the army coming along the north bank of the river from Blois. They rode quietly along, keeping to the fields, alert lest the English attempt a sortie, even at this early hour.

"It's not like Talbot," said La Hire. "He had opportunity a-plenty during the past four days to attack us. Yet he has held off all the time."

The other captains agreed and fell to discussing the events of recent days. The Maid cantered on ahead; she wanted to be first to greet le Bâtard, gone since early on Sunday to hurry up the army and recruit further reinforcements. She had spoken to him so curtly on Saturday last, when she and La Hire were for immediate attack on the English, a course the Commander opposed, saying that his advice was to await the return of the army. She had turned on him hotly: "You have your advice, I have mine," she told him. And later that day when the peppery old Sire de Gamaches had lost his temper over what he called the "advice of a stupid chatterbox"—to which le Bâtard seemed to pay more heed than to the "tried counsel of a veteran knight"—and had resigned in high dudgeon, it was le Bâtard and La Hire who had effected a reconciliation. She disagreed on many military matters with the Commander, but she was grateful to him for his unfailing championship of her, and she knew that for one of his civil and military rank he had shown her a consideration far beyond what might be expected.

"No further word of your herald, Maid?" a captain asked.

"No. But they did not burn him yet."

"They cannot burn a herald. It's against the rules of war. You will find that they have sent to the University of Paris for advice in the matter. We may have the English routed and your herald freed before they get a reply."

The Maid's two heralds had been despatched on the Saturday to the English camp to bear a last warning to Talbot. Jeanne did not wish to shed blood. She wanted her enemies to go away peacefully while there was yet time. One herald they held, threatening to burn him; the other they returned with Talbot's compliments to the Witch of Lorraine, also known to them as the Harlot of the Armagnacs—she whom, if ever they captured her, the English intended to burn at the stake. As she rode along, Jeanne could again feel the waves of shame and anger that had overwhelmed her; the hot tears she had shed. On the same evening she had stood on the bridge, and called aloud on the captain of the strongest of the English forts, bidding him and his men go in peace. And again she had been called foul names, told to go home to Lorraine and herd her cows, and warned that, if caught, a fire of faggots would be her lot.

Sunday and the ensuing Rogation Days had been

comparatively uneventful, except for the crowds that
followed her about wherever she went, waiting long
hours outside Jacques Boucher's house in hopes of seeing her emerge. La Hire, who could not brook inactivity
for any length of time, was engaged in a couple of
skirmishes during those days. She herself had ridden out
surveying the enemy positions. That a girl reared in a
remote valley, unpractised, untaught in the art of war,
could make sound observations as to the military strategy
to be employed when attacking, amazed the captains of
the garrison. That the English, who were aware that a
great force was being marched against them, should let
her pass by without attempting to capture her, was inexplicable to all. As the Maid with her five hundred
rode out on the Wednesday morning, the soldiers talked
of nothing but *la bonne Lorraine*.

Lances shining in the distance told that the army was
coming. Around the bend of the river came Friar Pasquerel and the priests, singing the Litanies for the Roga-
tions as they came:

"From plague, famine and war," chanted the priests.

"O Lord, deliver us," responded the soldiers.

"From everlasting death,"

"O Lord, deliver us."

"Through Thy holy resurrection,"

"O Lord, deliver us."

"Through Thine admirable ascension,"

"O Lord, deliver us."

"That thou wouldst vouchsafe to give peace and true
concord to Christian kings and princes" . . . "We beseech Thee hear us."

"That Thou wouldst vouchsafe to grant peace and unity to all Christian people" . . . "We beseech Thee hear us."

Le Bâtard was glad to see the Maid and the captains riding to meet him: he had been anxious lest any disputes arise in his absence; it took all his tact and eloquence to persuade some of the more haughty commanders to accept this girl and the guidance she claimed to bring. But without her influence, no one could hope to keep the army together. In the history of the Hundred Years War, since Harry of Monmouth, there never had been such a leader of men as this Maid. The great shout of joy that went up now from the ranks marching behind was proof of the soldiers' allegiance to her. They would follow her through fire and water.

"Greetings, Sire!" cried Jeanne. "What news?"

"I have brought the army back as you bade me," replied the other, smiling, "all good men still, penitent and shriven. But Falstaff, he who defeated us last Shrove-tide at the Battle of Herrings, he is approaching from Paris at the head of a large force; he's but a day's march distant."

They proceeded towards Orleans, where the citizens awaited in some trepidation, wondering would the arrival of the French army precipitate a desperate English assault on the town. Those who had marched all night announced their intention of snatching a little sleep. Before the Commander left, Jeanne drew him aside. "I command you, Sire Bâtard, in God's name, to let me know when Falstaff arrives. If he passes without my knowledge—I'll have your head."

"Fear not; I'll let you know when we sight him. D'Aulon! Stay with the Maid. I do not wish her to remain unguarded," and he went away.

Madame Boucher dozed, d'Aulon dozed; Jeanne slept also, but not for long. Suddenly she sprang up, shaking d'Aulon and Madame Boucher by turns, bidding them fasten on her harness. "My Voices have told me that French blood is flowing!" she cried. From the streets came confirmation of her words. "The English are slaughtering our men!" Rushing to horse, Jeanne, followed by d'Aulon, found a battle in progress at one of the forts held by the English. It was her first sight at close quarters of bloodshed and death. The French were obviously getting the worst of the encounter; men whose wounds gushed blood were being borne from the fray. "The sight of French blood being shed makes my hair stand on end," she remarked to d'Aulon as she reined in her horse to allow the wounded to be carried past. Then, putting spurs to the charger, she hastened to encourage her soldiers. "Fight boldly and with courage," she shouted. "Attack without fear." And the army obeyed her, making such a vigorous onslaught that in a short time the fort was taken, one hundred and more English soldiers being killed, forty taken prisoner, and the English tents and defences in the area of that fort, burned and demolished.

Chapter Seven

O N THAT Ascension eve, La Hire, le Bâtard, and the captains were jubilant. On the evening the Maid had first come to Orleans the wind had veered to a favourable point; now the tide of battle was turning, the capture of the fort of St. Loup being the first victory gained over the English since the siege started.

But Jeanne did not join in the general rejoicing; her soul was greatly troubled. How had it fared with those English who had been killed in the skirmish? When Our Lord celebrated His Ascension on the morrow, how many of them would be in Heaven to rejoice with Him? War was a fearful thing, the cause of many dying without those last rites to which every Christian was entitled. Perhaps she was in part responsible for these *Goddams*—gone before God so suddenly, and some maybe ill-prepared. She went to seek Friar Pasquerel. Meanwhile the captains discussed the victory.

"The *Goddams* fight well," observed La Hire.

"They are not the dullards we thought them to be," said le Bâtard. "It was a clever thought those fellows had who ran up into the bell-tower of St. Loup and donned priestly vestments. How were they to know that it's long now since Mass was offered there? If the good Canons were still there we'd have been rightly fooled; one of those *Goddams* sang the Latin as well as any cleric."

"Only for the Maid it would have gone ill with them," La Hire sounded as though he regretted her intervention; "when our men-at-arms dragged them out she pretended to treat the matter as a joke. 'We cannot harm anyone wearing the holy vestments,' she said. Her word saved their lives. She cannot bear bloodshed."

The captains agreed that the following morning would be the time to attack. Talbot was obviously disinclined to fight; when he set out to attempt to rescue St. Loup, the sight of six hundred French troops making ready to come against him was sufficient to make him withdraw. The prisoners told of the horror the *Goddams* had of the Maid; they feared her as a witch. Tomorrow morning, after the Mass of the Ascension, would be the best time to attack a demoralised enemy, the captains said.

But Jeanne would have no fighting on Ascension Day. If orders had to be given for that day, she would wish that they be concerned wholly with spiritual matters. Confession and Holy Communion for all the army; a warning for those who were rumoured to be finding consolation in Orleans for the camp women sent away at Blois. God had shown them what they could do against the enemy when they hearkened to His commands; if there was to be backsliding now, God would abandon them again. Though the captains thought the Maid was making a great mistake, they decided not to engage in battle the next day. She would not go into battle, she said, so perhaps it might be better not to go without her. Who knew what the soldiers would do when they discovered that she was not there to lead them?

Next morning, the captains took advantage of the fact that Jeanne would attend all the Masses being celebrated in honour of the feast, to adjourn to the house of Jacques Boucher, where they held a Council of War. La Hire, le Bâtard, and all the maréchals and captains were there—even the Scot they had nick-named *Canède;* Sir Hugh Kennedy, the English called him, but in his own land he was called the barbarous name Aodh-tar-leis-an-bpingin, Hugh-come-with-the-penny. Canède was at the Council and thoroughly agreed with the French captains that it was a major mistake on the part of the Maid not to attack at once. The meeting decided to make proper plans in accordance with accepted military strategy. The soldiers would follow the Maid to Heaven or to Hell, and for that she was invaluable, but—she had no plans. She admitted as much when questioned. How could anyone expect a seventeen-year-old peasant lass from the back of beyond to devise tactics for the raising of the siege of Orleans? Yes, it behoved them to make the plans; then they would acquaint her with the proposed method of attack—well, maybe not with all the details; she should be told as much as was necessary for her to know.

When they had made their decisions they sent for her. She came and listened while they told her of the proposed campaign—as much as they deemed necessary. But

she was displeased and would not accept the seat Canède
proffered her; she looked reproachfully at La Hire and
le Bâtard.

"Now tell me your *real* decisions," she demanded. "I
can keep a secret greater than that. I *have* kept secrets
greater far," and she walked up and down the room,
exceedingly angry.

Everyone knew that she had kept the secret she told
the Dauphin in Chinon; it was common talk that a thousand traps had been set for her in Poitiers and elsewhere
to make her reveal whatever message Heaven had given
her for Charles. The members of the Council of War
stared at one another in consternation. How deal with a
seer who knew what went on in secret conclave?

The Commander of Orleans rose and went to her.
"Don't get angry, Maid," he pleaded, and he explained
the full plan, giving the reasons why he and his fellow-
captains thought it good.

Somewhat mollified, she agreed, but councils and
council-chambers were not to her liking, so she made no
further delay there. Out in the clear air of the May
noonday she decided to make another attempt to save
her herald; besides, there was a last letter to write to the
English.

Jacques Boucher having put the Duke of Orleans' own
scrivener at her disposal, she dictated her letter to Talbot.
Even as she spoke the words to him, she wondered at the
great things God saw fit to entrust to her, an unlearned,
ignorant creature, Jeanne d'Arc, the Maid from Domrémy. All the while since she had begun to obey her
Voices, with every task that was commanded her, had

come the power of accomplishing it. How great was God! If He accomplished such wonders in an ordinary peasant-girl like herself, what would He not do in the holy and the learned? Here she was, giving testimony before rulers and feeling neither ashamed nor embarrassed.

The letter ran:

> "Englishmen, who have no right to be in this realm of France, the King of Heaven commands through me, Jeanne the Maid, that you abandon your forts and return to the land where you belong. If you fail to obey, I will raise a great *hay-hay* that will be remembered forever. I write for the third time. It is the last letter I write you. JHESUS MARIA, Jehanne la Pucelle."

The postscript concerned the imprisoned herald:

> "I would have sent my letter in a more honourable manner, but you detain my herald, Guienne. Return him and I will send back some of the prisoners taken at St. Loup; they are not all dead."

A crossbow man shot the arrow into the English encampment, where it was picked up and read; its message was received with loud jeers. "News from the cowgirl," cried the *Goddams*, "the Armagnac harlot sends yet another letter." And they yelled abuse and foul names in the direction the arrow had come from. Names that reflected on her purity never failed to cause Jeanne tears; this time she wept more than ever. But, suddenly, an inexplicable comfort came to her; drying her eyes she went in search of Friar Pasquerel to tell him to rise even earlier on the Friday; she wanted Mass offered early, and she would confess before Mass. She could never understand those who scoffed at her frequent confessions; the more one realised how great and how holy God was, the more one realised the need for purifying oneself of even the smallest stains.

The first half of Friday went by all too slowly for Jeanne. Unable to reconcile her ideas of what war should be with the conventional pattern of the times, she was eager to attack while sallies, feints, arrays and all the other gambits decided upon by the captains the previous day were tediously carried out. In the afternoon La Hire and the Maid went across the river by the pontoon bridge, taking their horses. On the far side some foot-soldiers, aided by civilians who were more enthusiastic than warlike, had drawn the English—like wasps from a disturbed nest—from the Augustins Fort. When Jeanne and her companion reached the bank, they beheld the soldiers flying in disarray, while the Orleannais got in everyone's way. There was nothing La Hire hated more than to see his side yield ground without fighting; shouting his battle-cry: *"Montjoie Saint Denis,"* he sprang to horse and, couching his lance, made for the middle of the encounter. The Maid, suddenly realising that this was how one led men, took a lesson from La Hire, jumped into the saddle, laid her lance in rest, clapped her horse's neck and rode furiously into the thick of the fight. Frenchmen, about to turn and fly to safety, checked themselves at the sight of Jeanne, her bright armour gleaming in the sun, her dark hair tossing as she rode, helmetless, straight for the enemy. Her clear voice called to them: "Courage! In God's Name, press forward! Forward boldly! Courage!" The men of Orleans, who had been falling back on the town, turned. The men-at-arms and Sire de Goucourt turned. By St. Aignan, if the girl God sent them was not afraid, who need fear! Were the men of France to be shamed for ever by a maid in her 'teens? To a man they turned and tore like men possessed after La Hire and the Maid. With sword and battle-axe they fell upon the surprised foe, driving them back first into the fortified fort of Augustins and then from the fort of Augustins and the fort of St. Jean le Blanc. Some of the *Goddams* were slain, some taken prisoner; some made good their escape into the Tourelles, the forts on the bridge.

As night was coming on, La Hire hastened to post troops at the forts just taken; Talbot might try to recover these losses by attacking during the night. Jeanne had been wounded in the foot by stumbling over one of the caltrops—spiked affairs used to impede the charge of an enemy; she was also weary and bruised in spirit as was usual with her after an encounter where there was loss of life. Returning from the scene of victory she came upon a fair-haired young *Goddam*, moaning in his death-agony. Flinging herself from her horse, she sent her page to fetch water, whilst she herself tried to ease the English boy's anguish. He was babbling his own strange language. At first he stared at her in terror—poor young Tam Langham, dying alone in a faraway land, with no one to assist him in his passage from time to eternity, but the one the men-at-arms called witch and harlot and worse; but she held a crucifix for him to kiss and her hand was gentle on his brow; and when the froth gurgled and bubbled on his pale lips, she wiped his mouth with clean linen and cleansed it with water—oh, blessed water! And when the pain grew less and the weakness greater and Tam Langham began slipping, slipping slowly into that sleep from which no man wakes, an arm kind as his mother's held him and a face as reassuring as that which had looked into his cradle was the last sight his dimming eyes saw. And as his soul went out on the evening breeze there was beside him one who prayed; and while he stiffened there in the shade of Les Augustins, there was a mourner to weep hot tears over his corpse, to fold his hands on a crucifix not his own, and to make arrangements for Christian burial.

Friar Pasquerel had been searching for her everywhere. He met her limping slowly towards Orleans, traces of tears still on her face. "The surgeon waits to dress your foot, Maid," he said; then, as her gesture towards the dead bodies on the battlefields told him the real reason for her distress, "War is cruel."

"I had no idea of how cruel it could be," she told him. "It kills and maims and makes hungry and lays waste. Faster than men can make, war can mar. It frightens me. It never seems to weary. And France has had more than her share of it; I wish I had never heard the word 'war'!"

At Jacques Boucher's, the captains were already assembled. They had been holding another Council of War. They sent Canède to tell Jeanne that, their troops being so few in comparison with those of the enemy, it might be wiser to await fresh reinforcements from the

Dauphin. The Council had decided to make no sortie the following day, Saturday.

"You have been in your Council," she replied, "and I have been in mine; believe me that mine will be accomplished, but yours will fail." Canède, much discomfited, retired to tell the captains her words. The surgeon and Madame Boucher were waiting to dress her foot. Friar Pasquerel made ready to leave. "Earlier still tomorrow morning," she told him, "and be ready to stay by me all the day, for I shall have much to do; besides, I have been told that tomorrow I will be wounded and blood will flow from above my heart."

Early on Saturday, May 7th, before the camp was astir, the Maid went again to confession. As was his custom, after giving her absolution, Friar Pasquerel gave his penitent some admonitions. "This is the eve of the Apparition of St. Michael," he told her; "you must place yourself and the army of France under his special protection and leadership today. Tomorrow will be Sunday, which you will not desecrate by fighting; ask your great patron to fight for us today."

"Tell me about the Apparition."

"I cannot tell you much—only the little I know from reading the prayers of the Church. At Vespers this evening the hymn will tell of the great battle between the angels before time began:

> Thy thousand thousand hosts are spread
> Embattled in the azure sky,

and at Lauds tomorrow another hymn will be sung:

Angel of Peace! thou, Michael, from above
Come down, amid the homes of man to dwell
And banish wars with all their tears and blood
Back to their native hell."

"How strange that St. Michael, so strong and valiant in battle, should be called the 'Angel of Peace.' But tell me more."

"When Gelasius was Pope in Rome, there was a celebrated apparition of the Archangel; but I am ignorant of the story. I only know the prayers the Church puts on our lips for the feast. At second Vespers there will be the Antiphon: 'O most glorious Prince, Michael the Archangel, be mindful of us; here and everywhere pray to the Son of God for us.' But I must make haste and prepare for Mass. I will give you my blessing. Think not of the wound you have been told you will receive this day; think rather of how great God is, and of that powerful Archangel to whose care He has committed you. Go in peace."

The Mass was sung at six o'clock, and at seven the fighting began. Jacques Boucher and his lady were distressed that their guest was fasting in honour of St. Michael. They tried to tempt her to take a little breakfast.

"This fine sea-trout, now, that was caught in the Loire only an hour ago——" Jacques pleaded.

"Keep it for supper, *Messire*," said Jeanne, laughing; "I promise you I'll bring back a *Goddam* to share it with me. And we'll come home by the bridge, Madame, with a fine appetite for supper." With a bow to her hosts she was out and away.

"Back by the bridge!" repeated Madame Boucher. "Surely she's not nine days in Orleans without knowing about the broken arches at the Tourelles! Win or lose—she can't come back by the bridge."

All day long the battle raged in the great fosse or trench below the boulevard leading to the Tourelles. Again and again the French attacked, fighting like madmen, rushing to prop their ladders against the highest points of the walls, scaling them in swarms. Again and again the English on the walls flung the laden ladders back into the fosse, wielding mace and battleaxe and lance on the heads of those who came nearest the summit of the walls. Glasdale, the English commander, had posted gunners and archers all about the Tourelles, to speed their deadly missiles on those who fell from the toppling, swaying ladders.

Unwearied, the Maid ceaselessly rallied the French, now lending a hand with a ladder, now running along the fosse shouting "Courage" to the men who had tumbled from the ladders, urging them to make further and greater efforts. When the mid-day Angelus rang, the fighting ceased for a few minutes; Jeanne said the Angelus with the soldiers; before returning to fight she thought for a moment of Michael, the Angel of Peace. How strange that God should so often call those who loved peace to fight His wars! Here was she, herself, who loved nothing better than the peace of the woods near Domrémy, hoarse from shouting war-cries, sweating from running about in armour, weary from exertion.

What did they in Domrémy know of real war, of bitter hand-to-hand fighting like this? Yet, God not only called her to this battle, He let her know, hour by hour, what she should do. "He taught her hands to fight and her fingers to war."

Flinging herself anew into the struggle, she ran to scale a ladder, when an arrow struck her above the left breast and she fell heavily into the fosse. The *Goddams* on the battlements cheered lustily and were about to descend to make an end of her, when some of the captains rushed to her aid and carried her to a place apart from the fighting.

It was a worried circle of men who saw the Maid weep and wince as they laid her down. Yet, in a moment, she summoned up enough courage to draw out the barb. The Commander sent for oil and lard to make a rough dressing; the others did their best to staunch the blood that kept welling up from the wound which was six inches deep.

"Go back to the fighting," she begged them. "Your place is with La Hire and the men at the walls," she told le Bâtard reprovingly.

"I'll return on condition that you promise to rest here. Friar Pasquerel, she'll obey you. Bid her rest for the remainder of the day."

"You must rest, Maid," urged the friar. "You have not eaten since morning. Drink a little wine and lie still until the bleeding stops and your wound closes a little."

"Very well. Until the bleeding stops. No longer." And she lay back, closing her eyes from sheer weakness and fatigue. Pasquerel walked up and down, reciting his chaplet and seeing that his charge was not disturbed. After about an hour the Maréchal Gilles de Rais approached; he had with him a foot-soldier.

"I brought this fellow," explained the young Maréchal, "because he has a song that will stay flowing blood; it is an old charm they use in his part of France. And he has a paper in the amulet he wears that has the formula for a magic brew——"

The Maid sat up. "Shame upon you, Maréchal!" she cried. "You should not encourage such evil practices. How do you expect God to help us if we pay homage to His adversary, Satan? Far be it from me to truck with black magic at any time—still less to heal a wound that God willed I should receive.

"Throw away your amulet and your recipe for the potion," she told the soldier, "and forget the song. There is more virtue in one word of the *Pater Noster*, believe me.

"Help me into my harness, Friar—the bleeding has stopped. And, Maréchal, wait for me; I'm going back to the fighting with you. How goes it with our arms?"

"Badly, Maid. All we can say is that the *Goddams* have gained nothing since morning—but neither have we. After the hardest day's battle ever experienced, things are as they were at the start. Le Bâtard is about to give orders to the trumpeters to sound the retreat."

"The retreat! He would sound *the retreat!* Take me to him."

The commander and his captains were discouraged; despite the Maid's promises, and after the hardest thirteen hours of continuous fighting any of them ever remembered, there was now no hope that the Tourelles would be taken before dark. It was almost sundown and the English were fighting as bravely as ever; the French were tired, and the men seemed to be losing heart now that the Maid was not in their midst. The trumpeters were being marshalled, when she returned to them.

"Bâtard! Bâtard!" she entreated. "Wait! Wait yet a little while. Give the men food and drink and let them halt from fighting and rest a space. Just for a quarter of an hour. I will wait in the vineyard yonder. Sound no trumpets until I return."

They saw her wince from her wound as she mounted her horse and rode towards the vineyard a little distance away. Neither le Bâtard nor any of his captains commented on her behaviour. All knew that the Maid had gone to pray; their hearts took comfort in the thought; they went to halt the men and to send them to find rest and refreshment, as she had ordered.

The English, weary after the worst day's fighting they had known since they came to France, took advantage of the lull to prime their weapons, attend to their wounded and take a little food. They hardly dared voice their hope; there had been no word of the witch since she had fallen in the fosse; if she were dead, the French would have fled long since—before that devil's dam came to lead them, they had been naught but a lily-livered pack of cowards. She must have been wounded sore—Harry Hawkes swore that he saw her fall with an arrow sticking from her heart. If such were the case, she would have bled heavily; every Christian, French or English, knew that once her blood had been shed her witchcraft would

be rendered impotent. Why had the French not sounded
a retreat? Why had they called a lull?

Alone among the young vines on the hillside, the Maid
of God knelt in prayer. Her Voices had long since
promised victory at Ascension. Why, then, was it with-
held? Not because of the army of good French soldiers
who had prepared themselves, soul and body, for this
great battle, who had fought furiously all the long day.
It must be because of some fault in herself or her prayers.
Perhaps she had not prayed often enough to St. Michael
during that day; she *had* said "St. Michael, pray for us!"
whenever she remembered. Suddenly she realized wherein her mistake lay. One should ask St. Michael to fight,
not to pray. It was at fighting he excelled, that great
warrior of Heaven. It was late; the sun was setting; but
what was sunrise or sunset to a captain like Michael,
whose glory was a brightness greater than that of the
sun. Many times now she cried: "Oh, St. Michael, fight
for France." And "Ah, St. Michael, it gets very late,
make haste to the battle."

And, from his high place in Paradise, the captain of
God heard the pleading of Jeanne d'Arc, the Daughter
of God. Touched by the prayer of this girl-child to
whom God said "Go" and she went, "Fight" and she
fought, the Archangel came swiftly and told his protégée
that her prayers were heard; he instructed her what to
do.

Obedient as ever, she rode back quickly to the
captains, who rose as she came. "My standard—where is
it?" she asked. A Basque soldier handed it over. Before
any captain could utter command or counter-command,

she raised the white banner, and rode straight for the fosse, calling "Courage!" as she went. Passing two companies of men-at-arms, she waved them to follow; "Do not retreat! Soon you will take the Tourelles. When you see my banner touch the bulwarks, attack and all will be yours."

Le Bâtard felt his heart stir as the white banner flew on the breeze. It was a flag to follow. He swung to the saddle and put spurs to his mount. La Hire galloped beside him, his eyes burning, his war-cry hushed on his lips. "Courage!" was the trumpet that brought all the captains racing and thundering across the field. Before, beside and behind them came the army of France, suddenly inspired with a new and almost superhuman energy. All, with one impulse, made for the Tourelles, where now the Maid's flag showed pale, fluttering against the grey walls. This time the ladders held. This time the French scaled the walls. Like the birds that flocked home in the May evening, the soldiers of the Dauphin poured into the forts.

The English were retreating in order; their commander, Glasdale, was fighting a covering action on the drawbridge that connected the Tourelles with the main fortifications. Glasdale had mocked the Maid. He had called her base names. Now he was fighting for the lives of his men—and his own, against her onslaught.

The citizens of Orleans, ordered by the commander to remain out of the range of battle lest they impede the military, could stay away no longer. Seeing the sudden change in favour of Jeanne's side, some citizens thought of a plan. To think was to act. In a few minutes, a barge,

laden with bones, faggots, leather, sulphur and other in-
flammable and foul-smelling combustibles, was quickly
towed out beneath the drawbridge and set alight. At the
same time, other burghers managed to throw ladders,
beams, gutter-pipes and trestles across the gaping arch in
the bridge at the town side of Les Tourelles. A carpenter
did his best to make the improvised arch passable. In
single file, the citizens, headed by Nicholas, Prior of the
Knights of Malta, scrambled over this rickety contrap-
tion and began to attack the enemy from the rear.

Jeanne saw the clouds of smoke roll up around Glasdale. She saw the green-tongued sulphur flames lick at
the dry wood of the drawbridge. The man would be
burned alive—he and those with him!

"Yield, Glasdale! Yield!" she cried to him. "You
called me foul names, but I pity your soul and the souls
of your men. Yield!"

But Glasdale fought on.

Some of his men, scared out of their wits at the re-
appearance of the witch they had thought wounded or
dead, turned and fled. Only a few stayed with the commander. The French, warned by the cries of their
compatriots, turned and ran back off the drawbridge,
leaving Glasdale and his men alone. With a great crash
the fiercely-burning bridge cracked in two, precipitating
the English commander and his men into the flaming
chasm underneath. A cheer went up from the French
army; quickly the news spread to the Orleannais on the
Loire bridge; messengers went running back to the city
churches and convent to have the bell-ringers sound the
joy-bells that would tell France that Orleans was free.

Soon, other bells out on the Solonge, and the bells far out on the plain of Bauce would take up the tale and send the good tidings pealing all the way to Chartres in the North.

That night the young moon rose to the sound of church chimes. In the woods the nightingales were silent, wondering whence came the golden notes that filled the air. Out through the Bourgogne Gate, the Renart Gate, the Bannier Gate and the Paris Gate, rode the King's messengers, mounted on the best horses Orleans had to offer, bearing letters sealed with a double seal, the seal of the commander of Orleans and the seal of the Maid. Orleans was saved. France was saved. The heart of the realm pulsed steady and strong again, renewing itself and with it the whole nation.

When the sentinels were all posted, and workmen had finished consolidating the makeshift arch of the bridge, La Hire made ready to return to the town. The Maid was waiting to ride back with him. As he expected, she had been weeping and praying for Glasdale and his men.

"They were brave men," she said.

"A good fighter, Glasdale," admitted La Hire, "but he should not have spoken to you as he did."

"What matter? I forgive him, as I hope God does. He did not deserve so cruel a death. The fire——"

"There's worse ways, Maid. I'd as lief roast for a few minutes as be thrown into a dungeon and left there to rot. Men have taken forty years to die that way."

"I'd face any death but fire!"

"We can't choose our way of leaving the world. If we

could, I'd choose to die charging into battle, the clang of steel the last thing in my ears."

"I saw where they burned a witch, near Gien. And now—Glasdale. If God let me choose, I'd choose any death but burning. I have a horror of it."

"It's your wound that makes you so morbid, Maid. All Orleans is doubtless searching for you by now and here you are, at seventeen, thinking of dying! What matter when or how we die—save only we be prepared."

. . . . .

Madame Boucher moved from room to room lighting the tall candles; in all the mullioned windows that looked on to the Rue des Talmetiers, she had placed richly-wrought candelabra, the sort used only on really great occasions—a family wedding, ducal or royal visits. The candles, when lit, reminded Madame of the Maid; they were pale and tall and straight and flamed ardently, just like Jeanne in moments of enthusiasm, anger or impatience. Jacques Boucher, standing on the main balcony, noted his wife's preparations with pleasure. It was fitting that his house, the house that lodged her, should be resplendently adorned for the return of the Liberatrix of Orleans. Like his wife, one moment he was jubilant, the next on the verge of tears.

"Marie," he called, "don't forget the sea-trout. You remember what the Maid said at breakfast when it was brought in fresh from the river. 'Not now,' she said, 'but I'll bring back a *Goddam* to share it with me at supper-time.'"

"She said she would come back across the bridge," Madame reminded her husband, joining him on the balcony. "Who would have thought that such could happen, remembering the four broken arches?"

They thought of the bridge as it had been this time last year, the finest bridge in France, with its nineteen noble arches and its row of houses on either side, its cross of gilded bronze, its drawbridges, its islands, its twin-towered fortress, Les Tourelles, near the far end. They remembered the retreat of the French across that bridge last autumn, when Salisbury marched on the town; the French destroyed two arches then, and the English two arches, at the Tourelles end. And just an hour ago, after sunset on this first Saturday in May, the sight of the Maid and her standard on the ramparts at the far side of the great fortress gave the Orleannais such heart that even the four great spans that yawned above the Loire could not keep them back. On shaky trestles, on pieces of gutter piping, on narrow beams and poles hastily nailed together to make lengths sufficient to stretch across the broken arches, the citizens, headed by Nicole de Giresme, had rushed across in single file, glad to be the ones who should deliver the *coup de grâce* to the enemy.

The other forts in possession of the English having been taken during the previous days, the fall of Les Tourelles—that fortress hitherto thought impregnable— meant victory, victory beyond the wildest dreams of the most sanguine in Orleans.

"I wonder will all those other things she foretold come to pass also?" remarked Jacques Boucher.

"She said that she would be wounded today, and that blood would flow from her body, above her breast. That cannot have befallen since she was able to lead the attack on the Tourelles."

"And you remember, Marie, she said that Charles will be crowned at Rheims and that the English will, ere long, be driven from our land for good."

"It gave me a start when she said to me the other night, as I undid her harness—'I have only one year, Madame; my Voices have told me; a year and a few weeks after Orleans is saved.' "

"They are coming! I see the torchlights!" cried Jacques. "But they are a good way off and great crowds block the way—hark at the cheering! Marie, we will receive her as we would receive royalty. This is the greatest occasion the house of Jacques Boucher will ever know. How fortunate that I had that new set of robes made, against the day the Duke would be set free from his English prison! I hope that no ill may befall him there now, in revenge for the victory his city and its Maid have won over the English." And "Marie!" he called, as his wife, already in her tiring-room, bade her attendants fetch her new vermillion velvet *houppelande* with the nettle green robe—the colours of Orleans—and her best and highest pearl-fringed *hennin*. "Marie! The trout. Bid them serve up the trout on the best gold platter, for the Maid and her *Goddam*." But Madame's attendants were busy about her toilette and it was Charlotte, attired as became the daughter of the richest burgher in Orleans, who gave the orders about the sea-trout. The little girl was glad to stay a few minutes with the *béguine*, watching the bustle in the kitchen, sniffing the rich odours of the hippocras and spiced wines, the highly flavoured potages and sauces. In copper-lined, claret-filled pans, pigeons simmered; on a long, slowly-turning spit in the courtyard beyond, a string of kids roasted; at the well-scoured trestle-tables maids whipped cream, whisked eggs and beat batters at incredible speed; whiffs of thyme and mint, garlic and peppers, came in waves on the hot air.

Shouting and cheering from the street made Charlotte gather up her skirts, and run to the entrance hall, just as her parents descended the staircase—her father, in ermine-trimmed cloth-of-gold robes, his chain of office round his neck, his fingers flashing jewels, escorted her mother, her silver-slashed green sleeves and green damask robe swishing as she walked to welcome their guests, her magnificent vermillion velvet *houppelande* falling in rich, sweeping folds about her, her *hennin* so high that it towered an arm-length above her smooth pearl-fringed forehead. They were disgracing themselves and their beautiful clothes, Charlotte thought, by weeping—actually weeping, when all were laughing and cheering—as the Maid, managing to free herself from the mass of people who carried her from her horse to the door, returned from the battle. Her armour was greatly smudged with smoke, and bore rust-coloured patches where blood had dried on it. Her face was paler than ever; her fine eyes blood-shot; but her lips wore a smile and her bearing was gallant.

Jacques Boucher bowed low and kissed Jeanne's hand. He spoke no words, but she understood better than if he had made a long and courtly speech. Madame embraced the Maid, releasing her as she felt her wince in her arms.

"It's her wound," explained Friar Pasquerel. "An arbalest bolt pierced her between the neck and shoulder, passing clean through her armour. Just about noon today she was wounded and she bled a great deal, but she was back again in the heart of the battle after a few hours. It needs proper attention, that wound; it was severe and painful."

"Come with me," ordered Madame. Bidding her husband fetch a surgeon, she took Jeanne upstairs, and, as on the first night of her guest's arrival in Orleans, she undid the armour and bathed and cleaned the wound while waiting for the surgeon to come.

"You would never guess who came to my aid and carried me to safety when the arrow laid me low," smiled Jeanne. "Old Sire de Gamaches, the same who called me a stupid chatterbox and was for relinquishing his command last Saturday, sooner than serve with me."

"Who pulled out the arrow for you?" asked Madame Boucher.

"Myself."

"How could you bear to do so? It was clean through, the Friar said."

"It wasn't half so bad as having to let them undo my harness and bare my body; they were gentle, it was La Hire and old Gamaches who helped me and held me while I drew out the arrow; I could not have done it so swiftly had I not felt so shamed."

The surgeon had a dressing of healing herbs ready and he and Madame Boucher bound the wound front and back.

"Shall you go to bed now?" asked the surgeon, and,

without waiting for a reply, "though Messire Boucher will be disappointed if you do."

"I will come down for a while."

The surgeon gone, Madame Boucher indicated two gorgeous costumes laid in readiness, one a lady's, one a knight's. "Choose which you will," she told the Maid. "I will help you dress."

"I may not choose," said Jeanne. "I am commanded from Heaven to wear men's clothes until—until——"

"Until when?" prompted Madame.

"Until the end of my year."

When they came into the banquet-hall, Charlotte could hardly believe that this vision in silken doublet and hose, shimmering satin tunic and cloak of silver tissue, was the same girl who had shared her bed each night for the past week.

"Eat, Maid," urged Friar Pasquerel. "Have done with fasting now that we celebrate victory. You need food after that wound, and the hard day's fighting."

But she would only have her usual repast, a little wine thinned with water, and a few pieces of bread. Why the predilection for such fare, Madame Boucher wondered. Perhaps because bread and wine and a drop of water reminded her of the Holy Sacrifice, of the Sacred Banquet of the Eucharist.

Jacques Boucher, suddenly remembering something, whispered to a serving-maid who hastened to fetch a golden platter from the kitchen.

"Remember your promise of this morning, Jeanne?" he queried. "You've kept but part of it. You beat the English—and on the eve of your patron St. Michael's second feast, too; you came home across the bridge; but you said you would fetch a *Goddam* back to share this trout with you. Here's the trout, and here you are—but, where's the *Goddam?*"

"Where's the *Goddam?*" repeated the Maid, in horror-stricken tones, remembering the English soldiers whom she had seen falling fully-armed from the bridge to certain death in the Loire far below; remembering the Commander Glasdale, who but yesterday had hurled foul names across the bridge at her; true, she had, in the very heat of battle, pleaded with him to yield himself and his men to that King Whose power armed her insignificance, Whose strength upheld her frailty; she remembered Glasdale and his men at that moment when the burning barge beneath set fire to the drawbridge where they fought the army on one side, the Orleannais on the other; she remembered them, when the drawbridge gave beneath them, vanishing into a yawning chasm of fire. Oh, how she dreaded death by fire, death such as these poor *Goddams* had suffered! And . . . perhaps . . . perhaps they were not good men, all penitent and shriven . . . perhaps they were even now in eternal fire. Alas, that she should bring such woe! Why had she ever left gentle Domrémy?

"Where's the *Goddam?*" asked Jacques Boucher again.

"I know not. Lost, maybe," was the hopeless reply, and regardless of the company and the occasion, the Maid of Orleans leaned her head on the table and wept bitterly.

Chapter Eight

I<small>T WAS</small> a fine thing to have a famous daughter, Jacques
d'Arc told his wife, Isabel. That remained to be seen,
Isabel retorted; adding that it would be fine if they could
call their home their own, a thing they had not been able
to do this many a day. All during the early summer of
1429 there were callers. Not an hour of the day but
someone was there, an uninvited guest; now a soldier
bringing news of how things were going with the
Dauphin's army—since Orleans, ready to follow the
Domrémy girl to the ends of the earth; now a friar
describing scenes he had witnessed with his own eyes and
which he knew would be of interest to the parents of the
Maid; again, the neighbours coming to hear what news
the soldiers or friars had brought. Even the Demoiselle
of Coummercy had called, and Sir Robert de Baudricourt
of Vaucouleurs. Now here came another; some important personage, this stranger, with a retinue of squires
and pages attending on him.

"Do I speak with the father of the Maid?" asked the stranger, stooping to enter into the cool, dark kitchen.

"Yes; and with her mother, too," replied Jacques, pointing to his wife who, seated carding wool in the light from the narrow doorway, had to cease now that the opening was blocked by this splendidly-dressed personage.

"I bring greetings from the Councillors of the town of Rheims," said the new-comer, reading from a parchment roll, "and an invitation to the family of the Maid, and to Durand Laxart, otherwise Lassois, of Burey-le-Petit, and to Jean Morel of Greux, and Gerardin d'Epinal, Jean Lingué, and Jean Barrey of this village, to attend the coronation of the Dauphin, Charles, to be held at Rheims come next Sunday if the Dauphin and the Maid reach there in time. The Councillors have bespoken lodgings in the inn known as 'The Striped Ass' in the Rue de Parvis for the party of the Maid's relations and friends, and a place of honor is being kept for them in the Cathedral of St. Remy." As he finished reading, the messenger of the Council of Rheims gave his document a flourish and bowed low.

"Rheims is over thirty leagues from here," observed Jacques d'Arc, non-committally.

"And we are poor folk, unused to staying at grand hostelries and unable to pay dear for lodgings at such places," added Isabel.

"The Councillors bade me say that you come as their guests. They pay all your expenses while you are in Rheims, and they send money"—he jingled coins in a purse he untied from his belt—"for your transport to Rheims and back."

Seeing that his hearers neither accepted nor refused, the messenger, bowing again, explained that he had to call on the others whose names were mentioned in the document he carried; when he had done that, he would return for the answer of the parents of Jeanne d'Arc.

"You will hardly find Gerardin d'Epinal or Jean Morel at home," Jacques d'Arc said, accompanying the messenger to where his retinue waited; "they travelled to Champagne some days ago. Chalons, I think, was the name of the town they meant to visit. They did not say what business brought them there, nor did I ask them."

"I shall ride first to Burey-le-Petit, and come back to Domrémy," said the man from Rheims.

"Well?" asked Jacques d'Arc, as he came indoors again.

"I shall not go," said Isabel, decisively. " 'Striped Ass' indeed! What godless names they choose for their inns!"

"There are such animals in foreign lands, I hear," observed her husband, in a conciliatory tone.

"I don't believe it," replied Isabel, shortly. "Do *you* wish to go?" she asked, her practical mind turning to clean linen and other sartorial preparations that Jacques' possible visit to Rheims might entail.

"Well—" and Jacques tried, without much success, to speak as though he really did not care whether he went or not, "it were well that the *doyen* of Domrémy be there; apart altogether from being Jeanne's father, I should be there, seeing that Jean Biget has not been asked, to represent the Maid's birthplace."

"How long will you be away?" Isabel was thinking of the corn already ripe in the fields by the river; of the sowers, Pierre and Jean, who would not be at the reaping; of her daughter who had worked so hard at last year's and previous harvests. If Jacques stayed over-long in Rheims, there would only be herself and Jacquemin to cope with this year's harvest.

"How can I say? Until the festivities are over, I expect. Mayhap I shall have our Jeanne home with me when I return."

Isabel d'Arc repressed a sharp remark as to her husband's ability to prolong festivities long after those who had inaugurated them had done rejoicing. She sighed at the mention of Jeanne. Her daughter was a cause of intense worry and concern to her; reticent by nature, she did not confide these worries to the other members of the family. No good could come of it; a girl of lowly station, on familiar terms with the great—it was bound to end badly. As for the stories of visions and prophecies and miracles that kept filtering through to Domrémy, they made Isabel still more uneasy in mind; a Christian who was on familiar terms with the other world was either a great saint or was already sold to Satan. And, in nineteen cases out of a score, Satan was the explanation, not sanctity. If her Jeanne had been a very holy person, used to speaking with saints and angels and archangels, her mother could not but have known it. Yet she, the mother, had thought of her daughter as of any devout and pious maid; a good girl, outstandingly good—but *no saint*. The very fact of Jeanne's defiance in running away last January—under false pretences, too—almost convinced her mother that her Mission, as she called it, could not be of Heaven.

Jacques d'Arc slipped out, intent on finding Jean Lingué and Jean Barrey before the Rheims herald returned, hoping to secure sufficient support from these neighbours to ensure his trip to the Dauphin's coronation.

On the morrow Durand Laxart, in Sunday clothes, came riding to Domrémy soon after daybreak. He brought word that Sir Robert de Baudricourt was travelling to Rheims himself, and would provide horses for those invited from Domrémy who might wish to travel in his company. In less than an hour Jacques d'Arc, Jean Barrey, Jean Lingué and Durand Laxart were on their way to Vaucouleurs. The harvest might have been non-existent, as far as they were concerned, so their women folk told one another. Their minds were on nothing but that tavern in Rheims, that hostelry with the strange name—"The Striped Ass."

Meanwhile, at Chalons-sur-Marne, two Domrémy men were waiting to speak to the Maid. One, her godfather, Jean Morel, could scarcely contain himself for joy and pride. To think that Jeannette, as her father had been used to call her when she was a little one, was riding on the right hand of tomorrow's new King—as they had seen her but an hour since when the great army rode into Chalons! Gerardin d'Epinal remembered how wroth she used to be with him for being a supporter of the Burgundians, and wondered would she hold it against him still. They would soon know. She had seen them standing in the throng, and had sent for them. Not like her brothers, Pierre and Little-Jean, two coxcombs of fellows grown too big for their fine leather riding-boots. When the neighbours from Domrémy had greeted them as they rode by, with a "Hoi, Pierre!" "Hoi, Jean!" they had ridden on, pretending not to have heard, though everyone could tell that they had both heard their names called and knew right well who had hailed them.

"A pity Jacques d'Arc wasn't here to see her," observed Morel, his thoughts following their trend.

"He will be at Rheims. They have sent a King's messenger to bid him and Isabel and others of Domrémy to the coronation; so I heard in the tavern yonder."

"Godfather! And good *compère*, Gerardin! It's good to see a Domrémy face!" The Maid, in satin tunic and cloak of cloth-of-gold, seemed a different being from the strapping girl they had known last year in Domrémy. Fine clothes made a great difference to the appearance of a young person; still, despite all the finery, she was the same Jeanne d'Arc.

"Do you think am I forgiven at home?" she asked, rather anxiously.

"Forgiven!" and Jean Morel laughed heartily. "You know your father. He kicks up a great row always—over nothing. He's as proud as a peacock. You'd think it was he relieved Orleans, not you! He is the hero—in his own mind, of course—of Meung and Jargeau, of Beaugency and Patay."

"Aye, indeed," corroborated d'Epinal, "he has fought that campaign of the Loire, not once but many times over. And far better than even you fought it. Your mother says that he was excitable before, but that now his daughter's doings have set him almost beside himself."

"They sent me no message. I was not sure whether they were pleased or angry," and Jeanne turned the ring on her finger. "Think you will they come to Rheims?"

"You may be sure that they are on their way there now, if the King's messenger has reached Domrémy." D'Epinal hesitated and then ventured to voice something that had been on his mind for an hour and more.

"Methought that you would have had me thrown in a dungeon when you saw me here—the only Burgundian supporter in Domrémy. Dost remember the day you said you would gladly have seen my head cut off, were it God's pleasure?"

"Indeed I remember well, *compère*. You vexed me sore that same day the things you said about the Dauphin. But let us not quarrel about it now; I never wish to hear of bloodshed—not even yours—I have seen too much of it. You will both come along to Rheims now, when my father and mother and others from Domrémy arrive. I have given word that you are all to be housed in the best hostelry there."

Delight at the not altogether unexpected invitation overcame d'Epinal. But he was a Burgundian, loyal to the end.

"Will Duke Philip be there?" he asked.

"I am sending him a petition," replied Jeanne, "to make peace with the French King—for we will have a king again, come Sunday. And I shall tell him that if so be he cannot desist from fighting—we know he is a war-like man—to fight the Saracens; but to cease besieging French towns and spilling French blood."

"You—you—will send that message to Philip of Burgundy?" Jean Morel's eyes were bulging. Just to think of it; good old Jacques' girl giving orders to one of the greatest princes in Christendom! As if she meant it, too. It was unbelievable. The same Jeanne whom they had all known as a little one; what a time she used to give old Papa Perrin, the sacristan, if he missed a Mass-bell or a morning, noon or evening Angelus; fair daft on church-bells she used to be; and Papa Perrin doted on her; everyone thought that they were grandfather and grand-daughter. And now she moved among the greatest folks on earth and berated the mighty Burgundy as though he were old Perrin.

"Somebody has to say to Burgundy the things that should be said." The Maid seemed withdrawn, remote. "After Sunday there will be a King of France. He will be the one to speak with Burgundy and others and tell them what the King of Heaven wills. Until Sunday I must do as I am bidden. It is fitting that Burgundy, leading prince of the blood, be present at his cousin the King's coronation."

"It will be a great and happy day for France if the Burgundians and Armagnacs do unite at last. What will you do then, Maid? Marry some fine maréchal or nobleman? Retire to a cloister?"

The Maid unwrapped something she had been holding in her hand. It was a tattered old red kirtle. The patches on it were turning purple, but she fondled it as though it were the richest damask.

"I had hoped to return to my father and mother," she said, "since war is not my calling. Better one day in the woods at home, than many months in famous towns. If I had my will, I would now be hoeing the garden at home or helping with the harvest, clad in this old kirtle, no doubt. Indeed, I kept the kirtle by me all these months, against the day when I could go home—my work done."

"And is it not done now, Maid? Will your task not end when the Dauphin receives the sacring oils on Sunday?"

"It is over and it is not over. But I am giving you this kirtle to take home with you from Rheims. It is good enough for wearing in the fields at the harvest. My mother will be glad of it. I had thought that I might return after Rheims—but I am not sure yet. I wish it were to be so."

"And when will you return, Jeanne? They will ask us that, when we go home from Rheims; every soul in Greux and Domrémy will ask us that. What will we tell your friends, Hauviette and Mengette?"

"Say that my time is short. That is all I know. Ask Hauviette to pray for me. Pray for me, you too, God-father, and you, *compère*."

"That we will, Maid," said both men. "You are not afraid of anything, Jeanne?" asked d'Epinal, suddenly smitten with strange fears.

"I fear nothing but treachery," replied the Maid, and looking into her clear eyes d'Epinal knew that she did not mean him, nor any Burgundian.

"But I forgot this!" she cried, rallying her spirits quickly, as she held out two purses, in which coins jingled. "If I cannot come back to Domrémy with you, who is to think of Hauviette and Mengette? Bring them each some pretty things from Rheims and buy yourselves a keepsake, too, from me. My father and mother, if they come, will have no time for going about the city buying fairings. And anyway, I shall want them to stay and talk with me. Good-bye, Godfather. I will see you in Rheims, *compère* Gerardin," and before they could thank her for the gift, she had gone.

. . . . .

The Kings of France were always crowned on a Sunday. Thus it was that Charles VII rode to his crowning in St. Remy's Cathedral on Sunday, July 17th, the ninth Sunday after Pentecost. To be sure, it was not Charles' doing—he would as lief have waited for the following Sunday, or the next, or maybe the next again; nor was it the wish of Regnault de Chartres, Archbishop of Rheims who, now that he had at last, in spite of himself, taken possession of his episcopal See, would have wished to spend a week or longer making detailed enquiries into the revenues of his archdiocese. As they had ridden through Champagne, a province which somehow seemed to have escaped the devastation of war, all had noted the abundance of corn, full in the ear, ready to ripen and yield a hundred-fold; the vineyards with their promise—was it not the land of wine—Champagne and Beaune—the cattle standing knee-deep in lush pastures. The Archbishop suddenly realised how foolish he had been to remain so long absent from rich Rheims, the capital of Champagne. When Charles had suggested loitering at Troyes or Chalons, it was My Lord the Archbishop who joined with the Maid in urging the dilatory Dauphin to hasten to his own coronation. But now that they were here in Rheims, the Archbishop would fain change his tune again. A coronation of a King of France—while the *oriflamme* lay in the sacristy of St. Denis, near to Paris—a place in English hands! A coronation without the glorious crown of Charlemagne—also in the hands of the usurper, alas!—and, for all they knew, now being placed by Bedford on the little head of the baby King of England! A coronation without the good sword named *Joyeuse*, the which weapon now reposed in its sheath of violet velvet in the abbey of those traitor monks in St. Denis! A coronation without the Sceptre, without the Rod of Justice, part of which was carved from a unicorn's horn, without the Golden Spurs, without the Gold Clasp from St. Louis' mantle, without—most grievous lack of any—the *Pontificale* containing the ritual of coronation! It was preposterous, declared the Archbishop, to think of having a coronation without the trappings fitting for such an occasion. Perhaps, with a little bribery, the Abbot of St. Denis might be induced to loan some of the so-sorely needed regalia, but it would take time and tact to arrange such matters. But the Maid was obdurate; it was a war-time coronation, she said, and when all France was united again and the English sent packing for good, then the Dauphin could have a second coronation, if he so wished. The only thing needful was that the King of France should be crowned in Rheims and that the sacred oil for his anointing be available. And, lo, despite all prophecies to the contrary, here they were in Rheims, the King to be crowned, the Archbishop to anoint and crown him; and, more wonderful still, the

English commander, when leaving Rheims, had forgotten to take with him the ampulla with the sacred chrism.

"We have had enough of delays—far too much dalliance already," declared Jeanne, and the councillors and burghers of Rheims heartily applauded her. They did not want this huge and hungry army of the King quartered on them for any longer than they could help. Let the Dauphin get his crowning over and pass on, King of France, to tour his realm. Besides, they were somewhat uneasy, remembering the subtle game they had played for some weeks back; sometimes running with the hare, sometimes hunting with the hounds, now sending messages to their Burgundian Governor, holidaying in Château Thierry, now to Charles and the Armagnacs, approaching nearer and nearer; now debating whether they should declare a siege and hold the town for the Governor and the English army that was promised to come to their deliverance within forty days, now listening to the accounts of how Troyes and Chalons had yielded to the host of 30,000 that was reported to be marching with the Dauphin and the Maid; finally—now that they again had an Archbishop amongst them, he having ridden in to take possession of his See on the morning of Saturday—deciding that they might as well have the King, and the Maid and the Court and the army and the whole bag of tricks. Yes, let the crowning go ahead, said the good citizens and prosperous burghers of Rheims, as they put away their blue white-crossed Burgundian hoods and donned their red Armagnac ones, and their well-bleached scarves, long held in readiness; and then God speed King Charles VII—before he got to hear of the see-sawing that had taken place in recent weeks—before the English arrived with an army. Rheims wanted no war.

So, on that Saturday night, the Feast of Our Lady of Mount Carmel, hammers resounded through the night, workmen and helpers bustled and fetched and carried and fixed, blessing the fact that it was full moon, the brief hours of the sultry summer night being almost as bright as the long evening that had lasted from the Angelus until close on midnight. On the Sunday everyone was up betimes, hurrying to the earliest Masses, murmuring when the priests embarked on lengthy sermons, a thing almost every good father in Rheims did that morning, for who knew but that the Maid or the Dauphin or the Archbishop or My Lord the Duc d'Alençon or other high and mighty folk might be listening. The text most of the preachers took was the opening verses of the 53rd Psalm, as read in the *Introit* of the Mass: *Behold, God is my Helper, and the Lord is the Protector of my soul. Turn back the evils upon my enemies, and cut them off in thy truth, O Lord my Protector.* It was customary to preach on the Gospel, but the Gospel that morning presented difficulties for a preacher, containing, as it did, the account of Jesus weeping over Jerusalem: *Seeing the city, he wept over it, saying: If thou also hadst known, and that in this thy day, the things that are to thy peace: but now they are hidden from thy eyes. For the days shall come upon thee, and thy enemies shall cast a trench about thee, and compass thee round, and straiten thee on every side.* No, it would be most impolitic to preach on that text! Friar

Pasquerel preached at the first Mass of the many the Maid attended. He took the words of the Communion for his text: *He that eateth My Flesh, and drinketh My Blood, abideth in Me, and I in him, saith the Lord.*

It was nine when the procession rode to the Cathedral. There went Charles, serious, not quite certain whether to bow and smile to the cheering crowds, or to give himself up to recollection and prayer. Jeanne, radiant, followed, her squire riding before her with her standard—that standard painted by the Scot, Hamish Power, that standard that had come through so much, and was now to share in such an achievement as the crowning of a King of France. The Dauphin's cousin, handsome d'Alençon, rode beside the Maid; La Trémoille rode with the Count of Clermont; other counts and nobles were in the procession—but the Duke of Burgundy was not there. And of the six spiritual peers, His Grace of Rheims and the Scot, John Kirkmichael—the same who had left Orleans to fend for itself in the hungry days of the siege—were the only representatives.

Jean of Metz and Poulengy were there; and the two brothers, Guy and Andrew Laval, noblemen of Brittany who had ridden to join the Maid early in the campaign and to whom she had made the fair promise: "I will yet drink wine with you in Paris." Not all those who had shared in the hardships of the fray could be there; La Hire was absent, so too was le Bâtard. They were fighting men, the two finest in France; comrades, though one was a free-booter and the other acting-head of the House of Orleans—a knight whose honour shone like a jewel in dark and dishonourable days. They stayed behind to guard the territory that had been won, riding from town to town, from fortress to fortress; sending scouts and spies now into English, now into Burgundian territory; receiving deserters from enemy armies and sifting the intelligence gained.

Jeanne would have liked to see La Hire's fierce visage, to hear his hoarse voice stumbling as he swallowed his oaths sooner than utter them in her hearing. She would have liked to hear the good people of Rheims exclaim at the handsome appearance and noble bearing of the Commander of Orleans. She wondered had her father and mother come, and if so, where they were, for it was impossible to pick anyone out among the dense crowds thronging the footpaths; every balcony, draped in the royal colours, held more than it was ever meant to. The colours of the workmen's guilds showed up here and there at the head of little processions of those who followed each calling; the civic bodies carried their own emblems; the canons of the Cathedral chapter wore their richest vestments, as they waited at the door of the almost-completed Cathedral, two hundred years a-building.

On the stroke of nine, Charles and his retinue arrived. A few minutes afterwards the Abbot of St. Remy, bearing the ampulla containing the holy oil for the anointing, rode his splendidly caparisoned mule up to the great front portal. His escort comprised four of the noblest maréchals in France; armed *cap-à-pie* and holding their standards aloft, they proceeded right into the Cathedral, up the nave to the choir, where the Abbot was lifted from his mule and his precious burden given to the Archbishop of Rheims, who waited there.

Long-dead spiritual and temporal rulers of France, bishops and kings and queens, looked down from the lancet windows where the morning sun, streaming at an angle through their stained-glass robes, lent them a glory that in life they had never known. From her high pedestal, Notre Dame de Rheims inclined her gentle glance on her children—on the Child in her arms, first-born of many brethren, on her other children, borne by other women, but, through her, born to spiritual life. On the high altar, where snowy linen gleamed, tall wax tapers stood like pale spears tipped with flame, priceless lace fell in frothy cascades, and tapestries glowed with *fleur-de-lis*, there were set out the offerings of Charles—a loaf of gold and another of silver, a great bowl of wine and a red velvet purse with thirteen newly-struck gold medals. And there stood Charles himself, wishing that My Lord Archbishop would hurry and have done with the tiresome business; it was really a blessing that so many of the customary trappings had been left in St. Denis, and that so many people who should have been present were missing; it meant that only the barest essentials of the ceremony would be gone through. He, Charles, could never have survived the endless antiphons and responses of the full ritual of coronation. And he would have felt insufferably silly hearing himself eulogised in so many psalms and canticles. The first one, for instance, when all those accompanying the King were wont to sing: *Behold, I send My angel and he shall prepare the way before My face.* Heaven knew that Charles was no angel. The crowd would have thought that those words applied to the Maid, had they been sung. In her armour, newly-burnished for the occasion, she was much more like an angel than Charles.

Through the silence rang the voice of the king-at-arms, calling his roll. He named the twelve peers of France. Of the temporal ones, five names were of houses now extinct, and the sixth—Burgundy—had not responded to the call of the Maid. After a few seconds' awkward silence, d'Alençon, the Lavals and three other knights, stepped into the breach and did proxy for the one peer in Burgundy and the five long-departed for Death's dark land. When the six spiritual peers were called, His Grace of Rheims and the Bishop of Chalons answered, Kirkmichael and other prelates present answering for the absentees. When the King had sworn to defend the Church, to keep his people in the Christian faith, to banish heretics and to rule with justice tempered by charity and mercy, he was clothed in regal garments, on his shoulders was placed the king's cloak, with its hundreds of golden *fleur-de-lis* on a ground of shimmering blue satin; he was anointed with the holy oil and, finally—at the end of what seemed to Charles an interminable five hours—he was crowned King of France. Then the voice of Regnault de Chartres, Archbishop of Rheims, rang out three times: "Long live the King!"

"Long live the King!" shouted the peers, clad in cloth-of-gold, their ermine-trimmed violet mantles falling in rich folds about them.

"Long live the King!" echoed the clerics and friars, the guildsmen and burghers, the beggars and men-at-arms. And the trumpeters blew shrill blasts until the very arches of the great Cathedral seemed in danger of split-

ting. And everyone within and without Notre Dame de
Rheims, joined in the traditional cheer, "Noël! Noël!"
as Charles VII of France repaired to the Archbishop's
palace for the coronation banquet. The first to salute him
as he descended from his throne before the high altar
was the Maid. Tears coursed down her cheeks as she
bent her knee before the man she had led to his crowning. "Noble King," she said, "now the Will of God has
been accomplished. He bade me relieve Orleans and lead
you to this city of Rheims, there to be crowned, to show
forth to all men that you are the true King, the ruler of
the Realm of France." And some, seeing the Maid do
obeisance to the new King, shouted "Noël!" all the
louder; but others wept, being filled with a sudden and
inexplicable pity.

It was a memorable day in Rheims. A great bronze
stag, lately ornamenting the courtyard of the Archbishop's palace, was set up in the city square. This stag
was hollow. The King had ordered that all Rheims
should drink his health, so the stag was filled with wine
and fitted with a tap and the crowds came to drink. At
every street corner stood great spits where oxen and
lambs, hares and poultry sizzled and browned. The
Councillors of Rheims were the only ones to wear
worried faces; they wondered if Charles, who had
ordered that the multitudes be entertained so lavishly,
would make any attempt to pay for the festivities; they
wondered how long the King would remain in Rheims;
the shorter his stay, the better pleased they would be!

It was not until the evening Angelus was tolled that
Jeanne managed to slip away from the banquet table. Of

all seated there, none had feasted so frugally as she; the servitors, honoured to bear her the golden platters, still found her—as course followed course—sipping the goblet of watered wine that she had asked for at the beginning of the meal; the little piece of rye bread diminished but slowly, as she soaked scraps of it in the thin wine. She was tired. The anxiety of the previous day, when at times it had seemed that Charles would never be crowned, told upon her now. The five hours spent in the packed Cathedral, standing in her armour, as erect as the standard she bore, her emotions as taut as her body—all the moments of that never-to-be-forgotten morning now took their toll. Heavy scents of spices and roasting meats filled the banqueting-hall; the aroma of the gingerbreads and sweetmeats was becoming well-nigh unbearable; as toast followed toast, the bouquet of the wines of Beaune and Champagne charged the already stifling atmosphere with their heady fumes.

She turned to the Duke of Alençon: "I must go," she murmured, "it is too warm in here. I cannot stomach the air. Make my excuses, good Sire."

"That I will, Maid. You slip out behind yon serving-wench and I will say that you have gone in search of your father."

"I *will* go look for him. It is now the Angelus and I have been unable to get away since early morning."

.   .   .   .   .

The widow Moreau shook an indulgent head as the singing in her garden increased in volume. That Jacques d'Arc was a lively fellow and no mistake—a man quick to realise when his star was at its zenith; he must have

gathered almost four score acquaintances into the garden
of the Striped Ass; treating them all right royally, too.
Ah, well, thought Madame Moreau, he might as well;
the town councillors' instructions to her covered any
hospitality the parents of the Maid might care to extend
to their friends. Alice Moreau had their orders in writing, so she was sure of being paid. Strange that the
mother of the Maid had not come. Probably the good
Jacques would not have been half so boisterous had she
been here. Who was this, knocking so gently but per-
sistently at the tavern door? Why—the Maid, herself!
Come to see her father, no doubt. And Dame Moreau
hastened to do the honours, receiving her young visitor
with many bobs and curtseys.

"I would speak with my father. He is here?" asked
Jeanne.

"Surely, surely. In the garden, with some friends," and
Madame Moreau would have ushered the Maid into the
garden, where the choruses were now getting rowdy.

"Could you bring him in alone, on some pretext?"
begged Jeanne. "I'd like to speak to him alone. There
are things I do not wish to speak of before others."

The widow nodded, understandingly. She knew the
ways of men—men of Jacques' ilk; he would parade his
daughter about in her fine clothes, strut like a peacock,
and embarrass this quiet girl before the crowd of wine-
greedy fellows whom he was vain and silly enough to
think were his friends. She would think of some excuse
to fetch him in; another friend from Domrémy; one who
wanted to have a word with him alone before joining
the company; one who bore a special message for him.

Jeanne waited for her father. It had been a long time passing—that six months since she left home. Almost a year now since that autumn afternoon when he had threatened to drown her should she ride away with the soldiery. Pierre and Jean had told her that he was lodged at this fine inn. Their mother had not come. Could it be that her mother, despite the ring sent her before Orleans, had not forgiven her? Jeanne wished fervently that it were her mother and not her father who had come to Rheims. Somehow, though he was fond of her, she never could feel at ease in his presence. She would as soon have thought of telling him anything confidential as of behaving or speaking disrespectfully to him. Why, old Perrin. the bell-ringer, had been told far more of her childhood secrets than Jacques d'Arc, her own father. It was almost as if she had no father; it was well that there was a Father above; whenever she felt the need of a father she had turned to Him—and He had not failed.

Jacques d'Arc found it hard to see, coming from the clear light of the garden into the dark, panelled room. But the bright-armoured figure did not leave him long in doubt as to who was there. His daughter's voice trembled as she asked, half-fearfully: "Have you forgiven me, Father—you and my mother—for running away last January?"

He laughed unsteadily, somewhat abashed before this child of his, grown almost overnight as it were, beyond his ken. This young maid who had hoed his garden and helped in his fields, who had stitched his linen and mended his hose—here before him, dressed as no maid in all France—nay, nor in all Christendom. "Forgiven?" she asked. Forgiven!

"There was nothing to forgive," he said. "We didn't understand; that's how it was with us—your mother and I didn't understand. Look at us now. Father and mother of the Maid of Orleans—the Maid of France."

Jeanne said nothing. She was, as ever, ill at ease with her father. He examined her armour, commenting on the workmanship and the probable cost.

"What will you do now, Jeanne?" he asked.

"I haven't thought," she replied. (True, her Voices had not yet told her what to do, now that the King was crowned; she would have died sooner than mention her Voices to her father; probably they would tell her to go home, soon.) "I expect that I shall go home to Domrémy now, with you and the boys. My work is done," she said, not knowing why she spoke at all—certainly not from any desire of making conversation with her father; she never knew what to say when speaking to him.

"Home to Domrémy!" cried Jacques d'Arc. "After this?" and he waved an expressive hand in a gesture that took in Rheims, coronation-day, Orleans and all.

"My work is done," Jeanne repeated, rather stubbornly.

"Done?" echoed her father, staring at her incredulously. This girl was no saint—only a fool! "Your work has only begun," he said, drawing her towards the window-seat. "This is the day when you can at last do something for your poor hard-working, God-fearing father and mother. Without the upbringing we gave you, those things would never have happened to you. Do you hear? Keep a steady head on your shoulders, my girl, even if it is a great day for you. Tomorrow the new King will start his reign by conferring titles and gifts on all those who helped to put him on the throne. What are you going to ask for? Make up your mind now. Such a chance may never come your way again."

"Father, I did not do these things with the hope of a reward. I did what I have done because I was bidden to do so."

"Even so, even so, Heaven does not forbid us take any rewards we are entitled to in this life; rewards justly earned; surely the highest rewards Charles could offer were well earned by all you endured for his sake?"

"But, Father, you do not understand. I cannot accept rewards for doing only that which I knew I was bound to do."

"You know that God Himself has promised earthly rewards to dutiful children—'a long life and happiness even in this world'—you were a dutiful child to us; you were dutiful to God."

"Yet, I shall not have a long life and happiness. I have not long left——"

"What foolish talk is that? You are but seventeen and a half; you are healthy. The Lord Who preserved you at Orleans and Beaugency and Jargeau and Patay, will look after you in any other battles you may have to fight."

"Father, I will ask for no reward. Nor will I accept any."

"So that's your thanks to your mother and me. One would think that a daughter grown all of a sudden so high and mighty would at least accept something for her poor old parents, even if she's too proud—or too foolish—to take anything for herself."

"If the King offers me anything for my parents I will accept it for your sakes—but I would rather he did not."

"Be a good, sensible girl, Jeanne, when tomorrow comes. That's all honest Jacques d'Arc asks. But—we're missing all the fun in the garden. Come and let's drink to your health. Maybe the King has some fine Duke for you tomorrow, and that it's a wedding we'll be having next; that's what would give you sense, daughter, a fine, upstanding husband like one of the young Lords who rode beside you today. If I were the King I wouldn't be long marrying you off. Are you coming to the garden?"

"Not now. Later, perhaps. I have—I have another call to make."

"Ho! So, there *is* a lover. But I won't ask you his name tonight. Tomorrow, perhaps. Don't stay too long away from the King. It doesn't do. Out of sight, out of mind, you know. Good-night, Jeanne."

"Good-night, Father."

It was useless. She could never open her mind to her father; he would scoff if she told him that the Holy Ones had been pleased that she had vowed to remain a maid while she was engaged in the work Heaven had directed her to do. She had not vowed for a set number of years nor even for a lifetime—though she had been told that her time would be short. A year and then a year; that's what they had said after the victory at Orleans, that time she was minded to take a house in Orleans, when Jacques Boucher insisted that she accept some gift worthy of the city and the raising of the siege. She had told him that she had thought of taking a lease of a house there, near the Cathedral of St. Croix; sometime, perhaps, she and her mother would come live there, but she could not say when. If the Treasurer took such a house, he could let it for the present and send the rent to her mother each Michaelmas.

Her thoughts kept her occupied until she reached the Cathedral, now quiet and empty, unlike earlier in the day, when every inch of space had been packed. How often, in the weeks just past, had she not slipped away from the field of battle to shed her irksome armour and bathe her hot and weary limbs in the Loire's cool waters; in like manner her soul slipped off its harness of cares and irritations, laving its weary self in that river of Life, the Blessed Sacrament, finding its peace and rest in those waters whose waves murmured ceaselessly: *Come to Me all ye who labour and are heavily laden and I will refresh you.* Along those tides one was wafted from the finite to the infinite, and, reaching the Ocean of Peace— that Paternity for Whom all paternity in Heaven and earth is named—the spirit of the Maid slept, while the lips of the pale body, stilled in ecstasy, framed themselves for the name they were powerless to utter—"Father!" To which unuttered prayer of one word, Notre Dame de Rheims and the whole court of Heaven made answer, "Daughter of God!" And the stained-glass saints and the long-dead kings and queens of France, and the stone angels, and the arches and the echoes all, in their own way, said "Amen."

Chapter Nine

THE TOWN of Moulins had a reputation for loyalty to the King. Three years before the Maid had come on the scene, five hundred noblemen and knights had met there and sent word to Charles, then living in wretched poverty at Bourges, a town thirteen leagues to the westward, that their swords and their lives were at his service. Charles would have preferred it if they had proffered him their purses. He owed huge sums to La Trémoille, he owed to his mother-in-law, to his cobbler, to his cook. The crown jewels were in pawn, the sleeves of his—the Dauphin's—tunics were new, but the tunics themselves were old, for his wardrobe was a collection of sorry-looking, patched-up finery. His table was poorly appointed and the viands often meagre and cheap—even a visit from Saintrailles and La Hire could not be celebrated with anything more succulent than a scraggy end of mutton and two old hens! But Moulins had been faithful in the days of Charles' distress; now that he was crowned king, it was a town where his army could be sure of a welcome. Marie, the Duchess of Bourbon, the great lady of Moulins, had championed the Maid from the start. She it was who sent word to Jeanne on the Feast of All Saints to come to Moulins with her men-at-arms and her captains and rest there while waiting on the war materials necessary for the siege of La Charité.

November mists lay on the broad stretches of the Allier that morning when the Maid rode up the right bank of the river from St. Pierre-le-Moûtier and entered Moulins; fully-armoured, she herself bore her standard. Behind came the Lords and squires and archers, the soldiers, blacksmiths and gunners, the tinkers and handymen, all the army that had been given to Jeanne's command when Charles ordered her to march on St. Pierre and La Charité. Slowly the parade wound up-hill to the ducal castle, their headquarters while in Moulins. The Duchess's steward and several retainers waited in the courtyard to show the men-at-arms their quarters, take the captains' horses to the stables and render such service as their mistress would expect them to give to the army in which her sons held high posts. The lady of the castle was not at home, the *béguine* explained, hurrying out to receive the Maid. She was at the Poor Clare Convent, down by the Geole Tower. Always, when the Blessed Colette chanced to be in Moulins, Madame La Duchesse —who had helped *La Mère* to found the monastery of the reformed Poor Clares—attended early Masses in the convent and remained to speak with the Abbess. But the Duchess had left orders that, should the Maid arrive in her absence, she was to be installed in the great guest room in the south wing. The *béguine* would be happy to bring the distinguished visitor there at once. But Jeanne, hearing that there was a likelihood of assisting at Mass, made her excuses and turned her charger in the direction of the Geole Tower.

After Mass she was bidden to a parlour in the convent where the Duchess awaited her. That great lady had not seen Jeanne since the morning of the coronation; she was anxious to hear a full account of the happenings since. Was it possible that King Charles had been parleying with Burgundy again, instead of continuing to press ahead (as all who had seen him crowned had thought he, the King of France, *would* do) against the English and the traitorous French who allied with them? Must one believe that Charles had allowed the insolent Bedford— that English commander who dared style himself Regent of France—to send him insulting letters without avenging the jibes against his own kingship and the Maid's virtue with the letters contained? And what on earth happened on Our Lady's Birthday in September, when the Maid and d'Alençon had failed in that assault on Paris? And was it true that Jeanne was seriously wounded on that occasion? And was it also true that the Voices had not spoken since Rheims, and that Jeanne had hung her suit of white Tours armour—the same she had worn at Orleans—on Our Lady's altar in the Church of St. Denis? And could the Duchess credit the rumours afoot that d'Alençon had been sent into Normandy with one army, and Jeanne on a wild-goose chase to St. Pierre and La Charité with another? Was it a fact that all her good captains—those men who would die for her—had been given commands in other areas, while La Trémoille's brother was riding with Jeanne?

But Jeanne would not hear a word against her King. She still had d'Aulun—the most honest man in France. And the King had insisted that she stay with the court most of that autumn; she had felt like a fish out of water going from one great castle to another; even the fine clothes—finer by far than the once-envied riding costume of the Demoiselle of Coummercy—even the horses and tournaments had palled. She had been glad to be sent to St. Pierre, and they had had a victory there. She was sure they would win at La Charité, too. But they were short of many things. Tomorrow, she would like to borrow the ducal scrivener, if the Duchess would loan him; there were letters to be dispatched to Riom and Bourges and Orleans, begging for powder, saltpetre, arrows and arbalests and other needs of war. And she would like to speak with the Blessed Colette; the holy Abbess was well known in Domrémy. Could the Duchess arrange for her to stay near the convent in the house of some respectable woman, for she was tired and in want of the balm of silence, she was harassed and only prayer could bring the succour she needed? It would help her greatly to speak with the Blessed Colette, who lived so close to God; of late she had been much annoyed by impostors who had claimed to bring Charles and La Trémoille, and even Jeanne herself, messages from Heaven. The Duchess did not attempt to conceal her disappointment that Jeanne was not remaining in the west wing of the château; but she knew of a woman, one who had once been her own tiring-maid, who now lived almost next door to the nuns.

She would go out and make arrangements to have the Maid lodged there and she would ask the nuns to request the Abbess to see Jeanne.

La Mère Colette was now nearing her fiftieth year. Hastening into the room where her caller waited, her tall, willowy figure made her appear as youthful as Jeanne herself. The Maid was fascinated and greatly impressed, as were all who found themselves in the presence of the holy Poor Clare nun; she wondered if the Abbess would remember that evening ten years before when, out of all the crowd gathered on the bridge near Domrémy, they two had been drawn to one another—the seven-year-old Jeanne and Colette of Corbie. Would the same undefinable attraction be there still? For a few moments the Abbess did not speak; she laid her hands on the mailed gauntlets, and gazed with delighted surprise on the girl standing so erect in her armour. Then she drew the Maid towards her and kissed her on the forehead.

"The little one from Domrémy!" she said. "I knew we should meet again, Daughter of God."

Jeanne said nothing; her soul was suddenly flooded with the great joy she always experienced when the Voices called her "Daughter of God." Colette's voice had been the first to call her by the name she liked best to hear. In the clear, resonant tones of the nun there were echoes of old days in Domrémy, memories of that day, a decade gone, when the Duke of Burgundy had been killed at Montereau.

"Be seated," begged the Abbess.

"It is awkward, Madame, with the spurs and thigh-pieces," and Jeanne indicated her harness.

But Colette had not been in the castles of Burgundy without noting how the great ladies had unbuckled their lords when they returned from the wars. She came to the girl's assistance.

"I will have one of our habits fetched," she said; "it will make you more comfortable while we talk. And some wine. You have not yet broken your fast. The nuns told me you received Holy Communion at Mass."

Before long, Jeanne was able to relax in a brown habit which, combined with her hair, trimmed like a court page's, had the effect of making the nuns who fetched wine and viands smile broadly. But *la Mère* and the Maid never noticed the gentle merriment. They had too much to say to one another. Jeanne wanted to speak about Friar Richard.

"He whom they gave you for confessor?" asked Colette.

"No. That's Friar Pasquerel. A good and saintly man. The other is a friar who was preaching in Paris."

"I have heard of him. He foretells the end of the world on a certain day, and says that Anti-Christ is even now on his way hither from Babylon. Have nothing to do with him, child."

"At first he was against me. When we met after he had changed from siding with Burgundy to riding with the Dauphin, he threw holy water at me, to see whether I were a witch or not. I said that I should not fly away. He is to be pitied as one not quite in his right mind; that was how I thought of him—until recently."

"What is it? You are troubled, *mignonne*."

The name brought back again the picture of the garden in Domrémy, where the scent of mignonette rose from the herb borders, close by the wall of the village church.

"Those who hate me in the Dauphin's court—and they are powerful—have encouraged Friar Richard to gather a sort of mock sisterhood about him. One, a woman from Brittany, whom they call *La Pierronne,* says that God appears to her and converses with her. And there was Catherine de la Rochelle."

"The Duchess spoke of her; in fact, Her Grace thinks that it is La Trémoille, not God or Satan, who is the power behind Catherine."

"I asked my Voices about her, when she first came. They said her words were foolish and her visions empty smoke. I asked her to come along to La Charité and fight, but she pleaded that the weather was getting too wintry. Then I told her to go home to her husband and children, but she would not. She kept on speaking of the white lady who appeared to her each night, and she offered to show me this vision. The first night I waited with her, I was so weary I fell asleep, and in the morning Catherine said that the vision had been there but that she could not wake me to show me. Next day I slept in the daytime and when night came I stayed awake. But no lady came."

"What did Catherine do then?"

"She hated me from then on. She spread stories that I was a witch and that she had seen two evil spirits come to counsel me. Friar Richard sided with her. He has not a good word for me since. He preaches against me. . . ."

"Never mind, *mignonne*. Those who walk towards God must expect to be attacked from the right and the left. What will you do when the wars are over? Or do your Voices tell you that you must fight for long?"

"Not for long, they said, 'a year, and then a year.' I do not understand, but that is what they told me just after Orleans."

"Will you go home when the year—or 'the year and a year'—are up?"

"Yes, Madame. I took a vow to remain a virgin while on this mission entrusted me by Our Lord. After that I shall do as my parents say. My mother wishes me to marry Michael Lebuin."

"I had thought that you would have been mannish in your ways, but you look womanly. Are you a good housekeeper?"

"My mother would not have a daughter who wasn't! I can spin and embroider and make lace; we were never allowed to be idle at home; we took turns in the house and in the garden and in the fields."

"So. Michael Lebuin will be well looked after!"

"But I feel at times that I will never go back. I think my Voices did not mean that when they said 'a year and then a year.'"

"Let us talk of other things. How long will you be in Moulins?"

"About eight days, Madame. The Duchess is arranging it so that I may lodge near the convent. May I come in often to pray in your chapel?"

"Come in the moment you hear the Matin bell and

stay until nightfall. This is a time when you are to rest soul and body. You must build yourself up for what is to come—when that 'year and a year' are over. The Franciscan Father who comes to hear the nuns' confessions will give you spiritual counsel, should you wish to speak with him. And when you come in each morning you will enter this room and doff your armour. Our habit will be laid ready for your use."

The nuns, who had been waiting outside, now crowded in to meet the Maid. They asked questions, they fingered her armour, marvelling at its weight and sheen. Jeanne was glad to be among women once more; to be in this quiet place, with no need to be on the defensive—physically or mentally; to relax in the company of good and holy people whose aim was to please God, not themselves or others.

The days that followed flew. While the nuns chanted Matins, she slipped into the little chapel. She heard Mass, received Holy Communion; conversed with *la Mère* and the nuns, sometimes with the Duchess. She walked in the convent garden, lent a hand in the kitchen and herb-garden, showed the nuns the embroidery stitches and lace-patterns of the Domrémy women, and learned to work the designs that different nuns had brought to Moulins, when they left the world for the cloisters.

She had written, on her arrival in Moulins, for help in this siege of La Charité. Orleans, always faithful, had sent gunners, clothes for the hard weather, several pieces of artillery, and a goodly sum of money to pay the soldiers; Riom promised money, but sent none. Some noblemen of the Berry country sent supplies of saltpetre and sulphur and a quantity of cross-bows. But the day Jeanne's army marched from Moulins to encamp outside the walls of La Charité, it was easy to sense that all was not well. The Maid, though fortified in spirit, was unhappy in mind. Of old she marched where her Voices bade her march; her orders came from Heaven. Now she marched to besiege a town about which she had received no counsel from above: her orders were from La Trémoille. She could hear the audible comments of the men-at-arms. Some said that they were being sent to risk their lives to satisfy La Trémoille's desire to be revenged on Gressart, the Burgundian captain, who had once captured and held him—him, La Trémoille, the King's favourite!—until a ransom of fourteen thousand gold pieces had been paid. Others said that the Maid was not herself, that Heaven was not with her in this venture, and that she seemed unsure what to do or how to command.

And there were those who suspected treachery. Had not the Maid spent most of her time in Moulins, not in the company of the Duchess, the King's supporter, but with the Abbess of the Poor Clares? True, the Abbess was a holy woman, but nevertheless the Duke of Burgundy and his widowed mother were her patrons. Colette could never have brought about her reform had not the House of Burgundy assisted her to make her foundations, most of which were in the duchy and under the temporal jurisdiction of Philip the Good. Why had a courier come riding after them from Moulins, bearing a spoken message for the ear of the Maid alone? What reply had he been told to bring back to Colette?

Who knew but that they were even now waiting for a Burgundian ambush—thus the murmurs and rumours went to and fro in the encampment, just outside the walls of La Charité, where Jeanne and her army were spending the first weeks of winter.

La Trémoille, who had been so anxious to send her on this expedition, showed no matching alacrity when it was a question of sending victuals or munitions or money for her men. Gressart, the commander of the besieged town, had decided to sit tight. Various deserters from the camp without the walls told him of how badly the besiegers were faring. Ill-clothed and ill-fed, the sorry plight of her soldiers was the worst affliction the Maid had met yet; but her entreaties fell on deaf ears, the captains and courtiers despatched to the Court came back empty-handed—the most they obtained were vague promises.

Advent came and with it an increase of discontent; not only the men-at-arms, but the squires and captains murmured. Were they then, they grumbled, to remain in this cheerless camp during the blessed and holy time of Christmas? When everyone feasted, were they, the troops of King Charles VII of France, to go hungry and cold? Desertions became more and more frequent, some making for their homes, others—banking on the probability of a welcome for intelligence from the enemy camp—crossing the fosse under cover of darkness and surrendering to Gressart, the Commander of La Charité.

By Christmas Eve the situation was so hopeless that the Maid gave orders to raise the siege. The previous evening, Pierre and Jean d'Arc had come riding from the court, bringing a command from the King. Charles wished the Maid to spend Christmas in Mehun, where he himself would spend his first Noël as King of France. A gift was awaiting the Maid there—one that could only be presented fittingly with full court ceremonial; on Holy Innocents' Day the King would give the Maid this mysterious present; meantime, he prayed her raise the siege and hasten to Mehun for the feast of Noël. Jean and Pierre smiled knowingly as they delivered their message, seeming to have some knowledge of the secret; they were in high good humour and could not understand why their sister showed no enthusiasm; she did not betray the slightest curiosity about the King's gift. She even appeared to resent being ordered from La Charité to Mehun. It was not like her to be in such low spirits.

"Wait until Holy Innocents!" remarked Pierre, slyly.

"It's not every lass has her King waiting to make her a Christmas gift," said Jean.

"I wanted but one gift—succour for my men. And that was only their due; God knows they have earned their keep and their pay, sitting here these cold winter days and nights besieging La Charité for the King. Now I must send them away, hungry and penniless. I want no gifts for myself—unless it is something I can use to pay these good fellows." And she turned quickly from her brothers and went to make arrangements for departure.

It was a grey, cold Christmas Eve, when the besiegers stole away, as quietly as they could, from La Charité. They left when the first cocks crowed, but though they moved as noiselessly as possible, their departure was not unnoticed in the town they were leaving behind. The townsfolk had joined the garrison, and were posted on the walls, hurling jeers and insults after Jeanne and her men.

"Go back, witch of Lorraine, and ask your demon friends to weave better spells," shouted one.

"Cowgirl!"

"Armagnac harlot!"

"Paramour of fiends!" yelled others. It was an ignominious ending to the expedition. The Maid rode ahead, alone. Her heart was sore for the four score soldiers gone marching back to Orleans, behind the artillery that faithful town had sent her. Eighty of the best gunners in France; none of *them* had deserted; not a man of them had grumbled at the wretched conditions; every one of them would have died for her. When they stood lined up before her, their nettle green tunics and gay vermillion cloaks the only bright sight in the grey winter dawn, it had almost broken her heart to have to bid them go back to Orleans—to go without striking one blow for La Charité. But they were good soldiers, faithful fellows. They had saluted and obeyed, going quietly as they had been commanded; and the last she saw of them was the green and red of Orleans vanishing like a torn flag into the foggy morning.

Jeanne's party had to travel fast to cover the twelve leagues between them and Mehun. Once or twice her brothers rode beside her, but, seeing that she was in no mood for conversation, they fell back again and rode with the captains. She was remembering the advice Blessed Colette had given her, not so many weeks before. "Those who walk towards God," the holy Abbess had said, "must expect to be attacked from the right and the left." Attacks from the left, like the jeers and foul names her enemies had flung at her, did not hurt as much as the attacks from the right—the realisation that her brothers, her own brothers, were nothing but a pair of opportunists, ready to curry the favour she scorned; the discovery that Charles—Charles, King of France—was neither all that she thought him to be, nor what she was sure God expected him to be. These were the thrusts that wounded one through and through. . . .

Trying to wrench her mind from contemplation of these painful facts, she suddenly remembered that it was Christmas Eve. In her anxiety over leaving La Charité, she had almost forgotten Our Lord. And what a time to forget Him!—at the very season when He most longed to be remembered. Some said that He came again on earth each Christmas night, His Mother knocking at the doors of men's hearts, so wide open to others, so tightly-barred to Him; so spacious for the trifles of earth, so narrow and cluttered-up that He—small though He made Himself—could gain no entrance. In Domrémy, hearts would be waiting to welcome Him this blessed Christmas. Doors would stand open, hearthfires would burn bright; every housewife would have her home swept and scrubbed, and all would sit around the fire until midnight; the festive tables would be spread, and Christmas would not be Christmas if some passer-by—some soldier from the wars, some strolling player, some Flanders merchant—did not enter; how happy everyone was to bid such a wanderer to step inside, in honour of the blessed Travellers for whom there had been no room in the inn at Bethlehem. It was her first Christmas away from home. How lonely it would be for her mother and father this year, with only one son, Jacquemin, to keep them company. And there would be no daughter. A couple of years ago there had been Catherine, quiet and gentle Catherine, who loved so much to steal away with Jeanne on Saturdays to pray at the Virgin's shrine at Bermont. Now there was not even Jeanne. . . .

The brief winter day was closing in. Already a star shone out, perhaps the selfsame one that had shone on the hills of Bethlehem where shepherds kept night watches over their sheep; maybe the same pale rays, serene and remote, had cheered the anxious hearts of Joseph and Mary as they neared the city of David. How foolish a Maid she was, Jeanne chided herself, troubling herself about reverses of fortune such as were the common lot of all who tread the earth. The only worry worth while was care such as Mary and Joseph knew on the first Christmas Eve, when their every energy and thought was directed to preparing for the Saviour's coming; their only hope that He might be fittingly received when He entered His world. Such a loving anxiety, so utterly selfless, would have added fresh fuel to the love the Holy One, yet unborn, had for His Mother and foster-father; that was the way, Jeanne decided, she herself must prepare for Christmas—no thought of the success of her arms and those of the King of France; all her thought for the King of Heaven and His cause—that He might not come and be unknown, come and be received not; that men might give Him room in their hearts. On such a night, so long ago, the good Joseph would have reproached himself a thousand times for his inability to find shelter for Mary; he might have said out of his misery of heart: "Surely the Almighty could—and should—have chosen a better protector for His Son and His Son's Mother than the useless wretch that I am." Just as Jeanne had so often complained during these past weeks and months: "Surely God could—and should—have chosen for Charles a better liberatrix than the sorry one He did." But there it was; God chose Joseph, a carpenter, for a higher work than any king or noble, any priest or wise man, had ever been called to do before or since. He had His own good reasons for choosing Jeanne to do the work that, just now, was coming all undone, going all awry. Who could know what were the thoughts of the Almighty, or why He had plucked her from Domrémy and set her among rulers and princes? All that mattered was, as Colette would have said, "to please Him and not ourselves . . . or others."

"There are the lights of Mehun!" cried Pierre, coming up behind her in the gathering dusk. The pleasant music of the court minstrels and musicians came floating out on the thin evening air. "It was possibly something like this," she thought, "when the Mother of God and St. Joseph made their way into crowded Bethlehem that first Christmas Eve."

. . . . .

By the morning of Holy Innocents' Day, Jeanne had recovered some of her good spirits. She had thought and wondered about what the King's gift might be. He himself had told her it would be something that would please her mightily; evidently he had planned to give her something that he thought would be especially welcome to her. She hardly dared let herself believe that it might be a grant of money and arms for the men, the very thing she had been beseeching him for of late; but that was what he knew she craved. Yes, she told herself for the tenth time, as she awaited the page who was to summon her to the King's presence, it would be a handsome sum of money, and an order to take the field again. Tomorrow she would be sending a courier to Orleans again, asking for her four score gunners and their artillery.

The page came. The King and court awaited the Maid. She was dressed as a knight of France, with cloth-of-gold tunic, satin doublet and cloak trimmed with miniver. When she entered the lofty hall where all were assembled, she noticed that Pierre and Jean were poring over a document which Charles was explaining to them. Her brothers, like Jeanne herself, could not read. La Trémoille stood behind the King; his face showed neither pleasure nor displeasure.

"Maid, come hither," called the King. She went through the usual ritual of bows and curtseys, unhappily aware of her awkwardness in court costume after so long a period spent in armour.

"Your Christmas gift," said Charles, handing her a parchment, sealed with green wax, tied with ribbons and cords of green and red silk.

"I thank your Majesty," said Jeanne, hoping that the King would remember that she could not read and save her the embarrassment of proclaiming her illiteracy before the court.

"Your brothers, being interested parties," remarked La Trémoille, "have just been looking through a copy of the document you hold."

"Just think of it, Jeanne," cried Pierre, "all of us—not only the men of the family, but the women also—all of us, and our posterity, are raised to the rank of knight. And we may take the title of *du Lys!*"

"You can call yourself the Demoiselle du Lys now, sister," rallied Jean. It was on the tip of his sister's tongue to hit back with: "I know no name I like better than Maid of France—unless it be Maid of Orleans!" But she said nothing; the courtiers thought that she was so overwhelmed with this unheard-of honour that she was bereft of speech. As one in a trance, she thanked the King, received the congratulations of the nobles. After all, she told herself, Jacques d'Arc and the brothers would be pleased, and all Domrémy. And the King meant well; she should not have expected anything in particular. Secrets, especially when they take the form of a gift, are always bound to be surprising, not what one expects, still less what one hopes for. When a chance came to withdraw, she quickly went back to her room, and, lest she give way to the tears that begged her eyes for release, sought refuge in swift action. In a few minutes she was out of the fine clothes and into her armour—not the white Tours armour, now rusting in the church of St. Denis, but the armour she had worn during the autumn campaign. She hurried down the stairs and across the flagged hallway. In an anteroom she could hear her brother Jean holding forth to a circle of young noblemen on the device that the du Lys were now entitled to bear, two golden *fleur-de-lis* with a sword between, on an azure field. Well . . . Jean and Pierre could be the two golden *fleur-de-lis*, thought their sister, with some sharpness, she was the one who would have to bear the sword.

"Where to, Maid, and in such haste? Riding to Domrémy to receive the homage of the good folk there?"

It was La Trémoille, who was standing on the steps when her page came by with her horse, accoutred and ready.

"No, my Lord." For a moment she played with the idea of saying nothing—a very wise course to adopt, she had found, when La Trémoille asked questions; but the old delight in giving an answer as good as the question prevailed with her.

"I go down to Mehun town to meet some children. It is Holy Innocents' Day, my Lord, and I yearn to meet an Innocent." And, putting spurs to her horse, she rode into Mehun.

Chapter Ten

THE EARLY months of 1430 dragged by, the heavy chain of their cold, wintry days slipping, with leaden monotony, into the past. Little happened to give the people of France anything to talk about. In January, Burgundy and the Lowlands had the third marriage of the Duke, Philip the Good, to occupy their attention. Bruges had seen a display of wealth and pomp unrivalled in living memory—which was what was to be expected from the richest noble in Christendom. All the old scandals concerning Philip ran the rounds again. How, people asked one another, would the Infanta Isabel—the young bride, to paint whose portrait no less a painter than Van Eyck had travelled to Portugal—how would she relish having Madame d'Or impudently queening it in Dijon or Rouvres, while she, the legal wife, was relegated to second, or maybe twenty-second place? Perhaps the poor little Infanta knew nothing as yet of what was in store for her! Her two predecessors had not succeeded in banishing the four and twenty mistresses the Duke deemed necessary to his happiness. What would King John's daughter say to all these fair ladies, or to the sixteen illegitimate children who would be presented to her? Doubtless, she had been acquainted beforehand of the existence of the three true-born step-children she was being asked to mother; but she had yet to become properly acquainted with her husband. The portraits of Philip which Van Eyck brought to Portugal would have given little clue to the real Burgundy; Philip's face was that of an ascetic, and betrayed none of his vices. Indeed, the Duke's proclivities were—his subjects had to admit—more in keeping with the character of an Eastern monarch than with that of a Christian prince.

As they regaled themselves with the wines of Beaune and the Rhineland, with the malmsey and rose-water that spouted from the street fountains during the wedding celebrations, the gossips of Bruges discussed all these matters. They wondered would Philip the Good—that was a rare joke, calling the Duke the Good!—would he, the rich, thirty-year-old son of Jean Sans Peur, live to an old age, or would he, too, meet a violent death like his father.

Tours, also, had a wedding that Shrove, a wedding important for Tours because the bride was a friend of the Maid. Heliote, daughter of the Scot, Hamish Power, the artist who had designed and painted the banners borne in the victories of Orleans and the battles of the Loire, was getting married. When Jeanne visited Orleans in January, she heard of the approaching wedding; it was a pity, she thought to herself, looking at the piled-up presents ever-grateful Orleans had insisted on giving her, a pity that they were all more or less perishable. Capons, partridges, rabbits, pheasants and the like—the only thing to be done with them was to bestow them speedily upon the poor of the city, for the Maid ate meat but seldom. There were fifty-two pints of wine—only that giving that away might offend the good people who presented it, the wine could have gone to Heliote. There was a doublet for Pierre—useless to Heliote; and anyway, one might be sure that Pierre would come claiming it. What a pity that no one had given her something she could send the girl who had been so kind to her during the tedious time last spring when the armourers of Tours were hammering the suit of mail that now rusted in the faraway church of St. Denis.

But if Jeanne lacked a present, she was not wanting in either initiative or good will. Her scrivener was bidden write to the Councillors of Tours asking them to see to it that Heliote was supplied with a dowry, or—at least— with a trousseau. Quite unaware that her letter had the effect of causing some commotion at the Council-table of Tours, she spent the three weeks while she waited for a reply to her request in picking out a small house which she intended to lease. Jacques Boucher and his good lady, on hearing what she was about, came to her aid and leased a house for her near the Church of St. Croix.

"You should have taken a larger house, Maid," Jacques expostulated. "This is too small a place for you. Where can you lodge your retinue?"

"I do not mean it for myself. It is a house to which

my mother can come in her old age. I have often heard
her say that she would like to end her days in a house in
a town; a house hard by a church."

"Even so, it is small. She will have you with her when
she gets old. And, wherever the Maid of Orleans stays,
there will be people coming and going."

"She may not have me. She may be all alone."

"What foolish talk, Jeanne!" interposed Madame
Boucher. "Of course you will be with your mother in
her old age. Or is it that you mean to go and marry,
when the English are defeated and the wars are all over?"

"When the English are defeated, Madame, and the
wars all over? . . . But if the King will not engage his
enemies in battle, we may not see the English beaten
for many a day. It may be that I shall be killed in
battle—not but that it would be a fine way to die, leading the men of France into some glorious encounter."

"Stop!" begged her hostess. "You make me shiver.
You are as bad as my Jacques. *He* wishes to die in his
sleep. Never a night but he betakes himself from our bed
to kneel on the flagged part of the floor, praying his last
prayers with outstretched arms. 'Wife of mine,' he says,
when I scold him for kneeling there in the cold, 'some
night I shall sleep and there will be no awakening for
me; not even your love will rouse me from that slumber.'
You are as full of morbid forebodings as he! Forget such
thoughts, Maid. You are but a girl yet, and the young
are given to such fancies. We will take this house and,
should you need a larger one in the years ahead, it will
be easy to take the house next-door and make the two
into a larger dwelling."

Hardly had the house been leased than the messenger was back from Tours. He had two tales to tell. The Councillors, after convening he knew not how many meetings, finally decided that the provision of a dowry, or even a trousseau, for Heliote was not a fit expenditure of public funds. However, for love and honour of the Maid, they had made arrangements to have the bride prayed for in the name of Tours and they sent fancy breads and white wine and red, to supplement the viands at the wedding breakfast. The second tale the messenger had brought was that Heliote had decided not to wait; while the city fathers wrangled about her dowry, she was married. Jeanne felt not a little disappointed at the messenger's tidings. She had thought that her wish would have been sufficient for Tours to do her a favour; it was not thus that the Councillors of Tours had respected her wishes last spring; she was disappointed, too, that Heliote, knowing how the Maid was making efforts to secure her a dowry, had not thought fit to invite her to the wedding. It was understandable for La Trémoille and others who had always been antagonistic towards her, to slight and overlook her as often as occasion offered; but friends . . . such as d'Alençon, from whom had come no word since the day he rode east to Brittany, and she south to La Charité . . . then Heliote, who had seemingly forgotten her in less than a year . . . and her mother, who had sent neither word nor sign since the day she despatched the ring by Pierre and Jean. Hurts from enemies were almost as honourable as battle scars; hurts from strangers mattered little; but the forgetfulness of friends, the seeming withdrawal of trust, friendship and affection by those most dearly loved, was harder for the Maid to bear than the wound the arrow had made in her body at Orleans.

Had she known it, she was only at the beginning of that road where abandonment followed abandonment. February and March dragged by; Jeanne was at Sully, where the King and court were passing the season of Lent. She fretted at the inaction; again and again Charles, instead of deciding to go ahead with the fight, signed an extension of the truce he and Burgundy had made the previous autumn.

Towards the end of March, new and heartening rumours were abroad. There was word of a great plot in Paris to overthrow the English. True, the plot was discovered and the heads and limbs of the leaders hung, grim reminders, on the city walls; but the fact that in the capital, a city thought to be altogether on the side of England and Burgundy, there were loyal hearts ready to die for France, gave fresh hope to a flagging cause. Jeanne could not bear to think of the patriots waiting and hoping inside the walls of Paris. On a bright spring morning she rode north from Sully, gathering a few fighting men at Lagny, a few more at Melun. They were mercenaries and had to be paid. Charles, as though he sensed it was the last money she would ever ask or receive, surprisingly parted with 12,000 *livres*; it was more than ample to equip her hired captains—Baretta and Canède—and their handful of men-at-arms, archers and crossbowmen. It would not have gone very far with the armies of La Hire, Gilles de Rais, le Bâtard, and those other armies—the hosts of France with whom she had been wont to ride. But, as it happened, the money and the men were not of much use this Easter. The Voices were silent. Like a blind person she turned now to Lagny, now to Melun, unable to take a definite direction or make a decision. What if the Heavenly friends forsook her too!

During Holy Week there was no fighting. For the sake of Christ, Who died on the rood, Christian men sheathed the sword; for love of the wounded God-Man, no man maimed his brother; no man's blood was shed in battle that week when all honoured the precious Blood that redeemed mankind. From Holy Thursday, the evening that commemorated such unutterably holy happenings, to the following Thursday, Christendom kept the peace of Paschaltide.

Jeanne loved the quiet days of Easter. On the morrow, she and her men would ride again. But, whither?—she asked herself, as she strolled alone upon the ramparts, gazing into the north-east, towards where Paris lay. The city was only eight leagues away, her men had told her. When she set forth in the morning, she would surely be guided; had she not prayed and prayed for help and direction during the days just past? God had silenced the Voices; but God had no need of Voices to bring about His designs. He would show her in some other manner where her duty lay and how she was to accomplish it.

Suddenly, the church bells which had been ringing seemed to diminish in sound until they were but a faint tinkle. Brighter than the sun, her Heavenly Ones came, their voices speaking softly, but urgently; this time they spoke strange words: "Before the feast of St. John at midsummer, prepare thyself to be captured and imprisoned. Be not afraid nor dismayed, for such has been ordained; bear what is to be with cheerfulness, and be resigned, for God will help thee."

And before she remembered to ask for directions as to what God wished her to do on the morrow—which way He would have her ride—they were gone. The delight at seeing them come again, at knowing that all had not forsaken her, made it hard for her to realise at first the import of their message. When, next morning, her soldiers waited for her commands, she signed them back towards Lagny; what mattered it where one rode now, if such things lay in wait. But at Lagny her men gave a good account of themselves and beat a band of English freebooters, some hundreds strong, who had plundered that part of the countryside.

Every day now the Voices warned; every day she asked about what she had been told at Melun. Would they be Burgundians or English—her captors? Would the King not pay her ransom? Would not La Hire, le Bâtard and de Rais ride to set her free? But St. Catherine only repeated the former warning; St. Margaret, when Jeanne begged her obtain from God a short imprisonment or death when captured, merely said: "Accept it cheerfully; try to take it well; meet all bravely, God will help you."

It was about this time that Burgundy, forgetting his Iberian bride, bethought him of his latterly-neglected war-making. That fool, Charles, instead of profiting by his enemies' inactivity, dawdled now in one of his châteaux, now in another, signing extension after extension to a truce that all the signatories knew well was but a sham.

Philip, sizing up matters, decided that this would be a good time to begin a new offensive, now that the Maid's star seemed on the wane, and Charles not prepared to offer battle. He ordered bows from Prussia; from Caffa, a port on the eastern shores of the Black Sea, came supplies of arrows, barbed and unbarbed. He mustered an army of four thousand Burgundians and fifteen hundred English, some thirty miles north-west of the town and forest of Compiègne; there too, came his artillery; his cannon named *Remeswelle* and *Rouge Bombarde*, and that enormous monster—*Houppembière*—that could belch forth huge stone balls. Many sappers, too, stood in readiness with their kegs of explosives; Philip intended to lay powder mines in a ring around Compiègne.

Compiègne was a jewel of a town. Situated a little distance south from where the Aisne joins the Oise, it lay on the left bank of the latter river. The forests of Compiègne and Laigne made a noble frame for the town, whose walls commanded a view across meadows that lay close enough to the Oise to be often water-logged and almost always bog-soft. To the east, beyond the hills, lay Picardy. Philip set his heart on taking Compiègne. Once his—this town which was, one might say, the key of France—he himself would be in a position to wage the war against Charles; he could do without the English. Holding a position north of Paris somewhat like what Orleans had held south, there were no relief forces expected, as had come to Orleans a year ago, no danger that the Maid would repeat her spectacular victory of the previous May. Compiègne might well mean the first step that would set Philip of Burgundy on the throne of France.

Although Compiègne had changed the blue bonnets of Burgundy for the white scarf of Orleans, and *vice versa* many times, its citizens were loyalists at heart. Its lieutenant, de Flavy, who commanded a garrison of five hundred men, was a brigand, more or less, and his private life far from blameless; but he was a brave determined soldier, one well able to hold a walled town. He made his preparations for Philip's onslaught; and the citizens were heartened by the news that the Maid was coming. During the first half of May she had been riding up and down the surrounding countryside, gathering men, seizing bridges and vantage points, so as to have the advantage if and when Compiègne was besieged. But those who rode with the Maid were perturbed; de Saintrailles and three captains who had fought with her the previous year could hardly believe that this was the same girl. Where of old she led inspiringly, ordering seasoned soldiers and commanders, setting seemingly hopeless initiatives that unfailingly proved successful, now she hung back and put the onus of command on others. When asked for a decision, she usually contrived to leave the responsibility to someone else.

Few knew of the temptations that tortured her—moments of wild panic when self-preservation urged her to fly while there was yet time. On the night of 7th May she lay awake, the full moon filling her tent with light; she thought of that night a year before, when she returned, weary but happy, to Jacques Boucher's banquet, while all Orleans cheered and sang and wept with joy in the streets. She thought of her good friends La Hire, and Alençon, both of whom she had loved, and the noble Bâtard d'Orléans, with whom she had never felt quite at ease, but whom she honoured as a man and a truly Christian knight. She wondered where they all were, and why they made no effort to come, in response to the letters she had sent them but recently. Of course, after that occasion when her letters to the citizens of Rheims had been interfered with, she knew that there were now none about her who could be entrusted with messages, verbal or written. De Saintrailles, perhaps, and the Count of Vendome were honourable, but the Archbishop of Rheims and La Trémoille seemed to be always visiting her forces and made sure that she seldom encountered the two captains. Looking out over the valley and the river bathed in moonlight, she remembered the nights during the journey from Vaucouleurs to Chinon, when she and Poulengy and Jean of Metz had ridden together. They were gone from her, too. Nothing remained on all sides but treachery and danger; the sensible thing to do would be to rise, while all were sleeping, and steal away home. Fifty leagues to the east, a soldier from Nancy had told her, when she asked him how far away was Dom-rémy. . . . But the Voices had said that God willed otherwise. . . . The Voices had said: "Soon . . . before St. John's Day."

Burgundy began moving in on Compiègne. He tried to bribe de Flavy, making a dazzling offer in return for his surrender of the town, but received the answer that the town was the King's, not de Flavy's, and the latter could not barter what was not his own. Then the Duke besieged Choisy, a small place close to the junction of the two rivers.

On 13th May the Maid entered Compiègne, to the great delight of the citizens, who lodged her in the Rue de l'Etoile and presented her, by the hands of their magistrates, with wines. But Jeanne had not come to dally drinking wine. She and Saintrailles and a force of over two thousand men rode out to capture a bridge nearby, which was garrisoned by the English, and which would be an excellent stand from which to proceed to the aid of the besieged people of Choisy.

Somehow, the Burgundians got word of what was afoot, and although Jeanne and her men rode out to attack in the early dawn, the Duke's forces came to intercept them, from a stronghold two miles beyond the bridge. Caught between the English of the garrison and the Burgundians in the rear, the Maid and her army had to withdraw ignominiously, fortunate indeed to get back into Compiègne with a loss of no more than thirty men.

On 16th May Choisy surrendered to Duke Philip. The only hope of driving him out of this place—so useful to him as first step in the taking of Compiègne—was to attack from the rear. To do so meant riding to Soissons, nine leagues to the east; thither, on 18th May rode the Maid, with her captains and men; the Archbishop of Rheims went with them. But treachery and disappointment awaited in Soissons, too. The captain of Soissons, up to this the Dauphin's man, unaccountably veered right round, and refused to allow the Maid or her army to enter the town. "We cannot have a force of that size quartered on us," he cried from the walls. "Go back to

Compiègne. If Compiègne wants you to fight, let Compiègne pay for your keep."

But the men who had marched the long journey from Compiègne knew that Compiègne could neither feed nor pay them for any length of time. And the siege might drag on for months, like that of Orleans the previous year. They broke up, each company going away with the captain who had led them to join the Maid. The Archbishop, smilingly, made his farewells. He had, he said, to go to Rheims, where episcopal business waited his attention. He hoped that all would be well. His stepbrother, de Flavy, would be sure to give a good account of himself in Compiègne. So he rode away, pride of place in his entourage being given to the shepherd boy who was reputed to have had more wonderful revelations from Heaven than any the Maid had ever claimed. He bore the stigmata, this lad whom people called *le Berger;* some thought him a saint, some said he was a half-wit, others roundly rated him an impostor. The Archbishop, who had so severely tested the Maid, when she first came to the King, gave a willing ear to the boy and became his protector, having him ride in his train; he even encouraged the people to approach and venerate the stigmata which *le Berger* readily displayed to all.

Jeanne rode back, slowly, to Compiègne. She had now but Baretta and a few hundred men. When night came they found themselves in a dilemma; word was brought that the English and the Burgundians had moved up to new positions; the night was dark, the moon being young.

"Let us press on and enter Compiègne," urged the Maid, anxious about the fate of those in the town.

"It is dangerous, however you go, Maid," said the messenger. "The Duke's men and those of the Earl of Arundel have occupied many villages round about the town, and some of these are so near the city walls that their churches can be seen and their bells heard ringing. Besides they have a great army, well-nigh six thousand men."

"Almost a score of them to every one of us," observed Baretta.

"We are few, but we shall get by," replied Jeanne. "I want to see our good friends in Compiègne, and by my staff I *will* see them. Follow on." And she rode on into the darkness. Along by the left bank of the river, through the forest of Guise they rode, silent, foreboding. But the Maid led them safe to Compiègne, the dawn breaking over Picardy as they rode into the town. Baretta had thought of warning Jeanne about de Flavy. He was, no doubt, a good soldier, but he bore a bad name otherwise. Rumour said that he had murdered his wife's father and mother, the more easily to lay his hands on their great wealth. 'Twas also bruited abroad that his step-brother, My Lord of Rheims, had intervened and taken him under his personal protection—had he not, in earlier days, introduced de Flavy to the courts of Rome and England and Savoy? Now that it was said La Trémoille and the Archbishop were trucking behind backs with Burgundy and the English, it made one suspicious of de Flavy. Apart from his relationship to the Archbishop, and the fact that he was under the latter's protection from justice, there was that horrid rumour of the double murder he had committed solely through greed. A man who could do such a deed for money might well sell a city as valuable as Compiègne—should the price be high enough.

But Baretta kept his thoughts to himself. He went away to sleep while the Maid went to the abbey church of St. Corneille, to hear the Rogation litanies sung and to assist at Mass, the Mass of the vigil of the Ascension.

She fasted till noon, as was her custom on eves of great feasts. Towards evening she called Baretta, her brother Pierre—who had been in Compiègne when she returned—and honest d'Aulon, her squire, and her standard-bearer. "Get our company together," she ordered. "We will make a sally and surprise the Burgundians in the nearest village. If we beat up their quarters, they will clear out and fall back, and it will be one enemy outpost destroyed. I have spoken with de Flavy and he has agreed to line the walls of Compiègne with archers and culverin men and crossbow men. He will also have boats in the river, filled with archers; all these will cover our retreat."

D'Aulon fetched a dapple-grey charger; the others assembled the men-at-arms; the Governor, de Flavy, began posting his men as he had told the Maid he would. At five o'clock the company rode out across the bridge, the Maid rather more resplendent than was usual for her in the hour of battle. Over her armour she wore a surcoat of cloth-of-gold, and over this again she wore a scarlet *hucque* richly embroidered; in her hand she held a flat sword that she had taken from a Burgundian soldier at Lagny. Since Lagny, no one had seen the sword of

Fierbois; it must be presumed lost or stolen, d'Aulon reflected, for the Maid had carried this other sword these last weeks.

Leaving the bridge, they rode across the meadows, making for the utterly unprepared outpost of the Burgundians; the latter scattered and fled in all directions, the Lombards who comprised most of Baretta's force harrying them for a bit, then returning to plunder the belongings left behind at the outpost. But Jean of Luxembourg, a one-eyed commander in the pay of the English, happened to come riding along from his camp higher up the river, accompanied by some of his gentlemen-at-arms. He thought that it might be a good idea to ride to the outpost, to see that all was in order, and, incidentally, to reconnoitre Compiègne. He was a witness of the sallying forth from the town and of the surprise attack. Sending a rider at top-speed back to the camp, he was gratified to see his forces approaching at the gallop and in good order in an incredibly short space of time. Shouting the Burgundian war-cry, he led his men downhill to where the Maid's men were looting the momentarily abandoned outpost.

The Lombard mercenaries were unwilling to leave their loot and were slow to obey the orders of d'Aulon and the Maid to retreat rapidly to where the boats were waiting in the river. Before many minutes the meadows became a battlefield. The Burgundians—greatly emboldened at sighting English detachments coming up to reinforce them, and greatly enraged at seeing their provisions, weapons, and personal belongings being carried off by the Lombards—returned and fought like demons.

Jeanne's men fled, some for the bridge, some for the boats, hotly pursued by vastly superior and better disciplined forces. The archers on the walls and in the boats on the river, unable to distinguish between friend or foe, were obliged to hold their fire. And as the onrush of the Burgundians threatened to be heavy and impetuous enough to menace the safety of the city, when de Flavy saw the foe at the far end of the bridge connecting with the Water Gate, he drew up the drawbridge and lowered the portcullis. Fighting a rearguard action on the waterlogged meadows was a richly dressed young fighter on a dapple-grey charger; there also was d'Aulon and the young knight Pierre du Lys and a few others. But there was no purpose now in fighting for the safety of men who had fled in all directions; no hope of holding out against the enemy who surrounded them.

The English and Burgundians had suddenly realised the identity of the rider on the grey. Rapacity possessed them. Here was one who would fetch a King's ransom; the ransom would go to him who took her prisoner; or if not to him, to his Lord.

"Yield to me, Maid!" roared many voices. Many hands snatched at her bridle-rein.

"Never!" she cried, spurring her horse and endeavouring to ride through the press that encircled her.

"Give your word to me," called one.

"To me," yelled another.

"Nay, to me," several shouted.

"I have given my word and my surrender to Another than you. To Him I keep my word."

Rough hands tore at her bright cloak; her wounded

mount foundered hopelessly in the water-logged ground; as an archer dragged her to the ground, she could see, through the hot tears that rushed to her eyes, Friar Pasquerel, her brother Pierre, d'Aulon and the faithful few who had remained with her, being bound securely. As in a dream, she submitted to similar bonds. The captain of the Picard archers who had taken her waited impatiently to fetch her to his master, Jean of Luxembourg. Already that Lord had ridden to Choisy to tell the Duke and the English Earl the incredible news. The Maid of Orleans was his prisoner.

Far into the night the cheering of the English and Burgundian troops carried downhill into Compiègne. The one they had feared more than any other captain or chief was not, after all, invincible; she was defeated, a prisoner in their hands. Now they feared no foe. Let Charles get whom he would to lead his armies, his enemies cared not—the Maid was theirs. It was only a matter of time until all France be theirs also.

Chapter Eleven

L IKE WILDFIRE the news of the capture on Ascension
Eve spread throughout France. In the camp where
the Maid was held prisoner, pending a decision as to
whose property she really was, the soldiers were jubilant.
The captain, whose archer had taken her, went about
receiving the congratulations of his fellow-officers, all of
whom agreed with him that they would rather have
taken the Maid prisoner than five hundred men. Duke
Philip himself, accompanied by his chronicler, Monstre-
let, had had a special interview with the wench on the
night of her capture. No rumour of what had taken place
at the interview got abroad. The very next morning,
after Mass in honour of Our Lord's Ascension, the Duke
wrote letters:

"Let all give thanks and praise to the Creator," he
wrote, "Who hath delivered into our hands the *Pucelle*.
This will be welcome news to all; it will prove how
foolish and how deeply in error were those who gave
credence to that woman."

Now that it had befallen as she had been warned, the Maid felt at peace. She had, so far, no reason to complain of how she was treated; d'Aulon was allowed to remain in her company, and they were lodged as comfortably as the Earl of Arundel or Burgundy himself, in a spacious pavilion, well furnished and with dividing tapestries that made several apartments. She was alone most of the time, having given d'Aulon to understand that she would prefer it so. He, conscious that they were probably being spied on all the time by the soldiers who ringed their tent, was content to leave her in solitude. In a day or two, Alençon, La Hire and le Bâtard would be bound to come riding to the rescue. Better, d'Aulon told himself, to rest and be ready for swift action when the time came.

Jeanne, suddenly conscious of great weariness, yielded to the lassitude which came over her, and rested and slept as she had not done for months. She could not bear to think that the King would fail to come forward with her ransom money; but the Voices had not spoken of ransom —only of imprisonment. She did not know whose prisoner she was; the Duke Philip had been to see her, and some English lords speaking together in their strange, foreign language; for the present they were not going to put her to the torture or to death. But what did the future hold? Other captives, taken in war, had been speedily dispatched when it was found that their ransom money was not forthcoming; and some had been imprisoned for years and years, living through youth, middle-age, and on into dotage behind prison walls. She did not think that she could bear that, even in surroundings as comfortable as those in which she now found herself.

The very thought of such a caged-in existence made her leap from her couch and pace up and down the tent, staring through the openings at patches of sky and tree-foliage; then she remembered that now, as on the ride to Chinon, as on the walls of Orleans, she was in the Hand of God, and she calmed down and rested again. Sometimes she spent hours in prayer—not praying for anything in particular, not speaking many words, but staying still, aware of God's nearness and power and holiness. In such moments the world and life and time itself—even this Ascension Day, this airless, tapestried pavilion, French friends, Burgundian and English foes—seemed to fade away, and she herself looked with a remote and indifferent gaze on all the things pertaining to her earthly existence.

Once, after a few moments' restless pacing to and fro, when her imagination had recalled stories of tortures and ordeals to which prisoners had been subjected, and when her memory of those days before the tribunal at Poitiers —a tribunal that was, in part, composed of men favourable to the King—warned her of what to expect when brought before a court convened by the King's enemies, she fell on her knees, imploring Heaven: "I am but an ignorant girl. How shall I answer when the wise and clever and learned men begin to question?" And, instantly, the pavilion became a bright, unknown shore, peopled with thousands of those who were, at one and the same time, strangers and friends. And they made known to her, without words, how they too had once wondered what to say before earthly tribunals, but One had said: "*Be not thoughtful beforehand what you shall speak; for I will give you a mouth and wisdom, which all your adversaries shall not be able to resist and gainsay. For it is not you that speak then, but the Holy Ghost."* And, while she wondered at the brightness of the place where these heavenly friends stood, they and the light surrounding them faded, as a few minutes before the pavilion had faded, and she was alone again, kneeling forlornly in the same place, suddenly dark and dingy after the shining vision she had just been granted.

But she felt strangely comforted and the memory of the vision helped her through many similar onsets of panic. Meanwhile the days dragged by and still there was no word of ransom, no sign of a rescue attempt. The prisoners knew nothing of what was happening—beyond hearing threats of the fate that lay in store for the citizens of Compiègne when that town should be taken. The soldiers guarding the pavilion told one another that the Duke and Arundel intended to make sure that Compiègne paid dearly for holding out against them and immobilising such great numbers of their troops. All over seven years of age would be put to the sword and the town given to the flames, they said; now that the Maid was captured, the English and Burgundians intended to wage a war of ferocity and terror; that was the only way to cow the French and their hide-and-go-seek King into speedy submission.

In faithful Orleans, as in Blois and Tours, there were penitential processions where priests and people went barefoot, chanting the *Miserere* and praying for the Maid's deliverance. The Archbishop of Embrun, Messer

Gelu, had a special Collect, a Secret and a Communion Prayer inserted in the Mass:

> . . . *Grant, we beseech Thee, through the intercession of Blessed Mary ever Virgin and of all the saints, that she may be delivered from their power without suffering any hurt and that she may accomplish all that Thou hast prescribed for her to do.*
>
> . . . *May this offering set free the Maid confined in the gaols of our enemies; may it liberate her free from all hurt and give her the grace to carry out effectively the work which Thou hast commanded her. . . .*
>
> . . . *By the sacraments which we have received, by the intercession of the Blessed Mary, ever a Virgin, and of all the Saints, let her chains fall from the Maid who accomplished the works prescribed for her, and who is now incarcerated by our enemies; grant, by Thy most holy and merciful solicitude, that she may, in order to accomplish the needs that remain, come forth from prison without suffering any harm, through Our Lord Jesus Christ, Who, with Thee and the Holy Ghost, livest and reignest, world without end. Amen. . . .*

But Jacques Gelu, a holy man who had been greatly impressed by Jeanne at the Poitiers enquiry the previous year, did more than pray and get others to pray for her. He wrote to the King:

> For the recovery of this girl, and for her ransom, let neither money nor possessions be spared, whatever be the price asked, so that your Majesty may not incur the undying shame of basest ingratitude. Get people every-

where to pray, and you yourself pray also, so that if this misfortune hath come upon us because of any sin of the King or people of France, it may please God to forgive it.

But there were others who neither prayed for her nor advised their people to pray. The Archbishop of Rheims wrote a letter to the people of his archdiocese, saying that the Maid had deserved her capture, being one who would not brook advice, but prone to self-will; and he quoted the young shepherd lad, his protégé, as having told the King "neither more nor less than the Maid." The boy also said, and his words were promptly repeated by the Archbishop in a second letter to Rheims, that God had permitted the Maid to be taken because she had become puffed up with pride and was much addicted to rich raiment, seeking her own will instead of the Will of God.

The University of Paris was overjoyed on hearing the news of Jeanne's capture. Clerks and professors came in procession to Notre Dame and joined with a large congregation of English and Burgundian supporters in singing a *Te Deum;* the University authorities sent letters to Burgundy and the English demanding that the prisoner be sent for trial in Paris, on charges of heresy, witchcraft and idolatry. Someone then remembered how the world-renowned Gerson, Chancellor of Notre Dame and one-time head of Paris University, together with the Archbishop of Embrun, championed the Maid after hearing her answers at Poitiers. There was much ado preparing arguments to refute all that the theologian

Gerson, now deceased, had written at that time in defence of the Maid.

The King, on receipt of Gelu's letter, sent a message to Burgundy full of brave threats. He had no hope of raising a ransom, being more than ever in debt to his dear La Trémoille; and, having sent the message to Burgundy, Charles did no more.

There was considerable delay trying to come to a decision as to who should claim the prisoner. By the laws of war she belonged to Luxembourg, who made a payment of some hundred crowns to his captain, who in turn threw the price of a few drinks to the archer who had taken her captive. But, finding one day that the Maid almost succeeded in escaping from custody, Luxembourg had her removed to the family fortress at Beaurevoir. There his aunt, his wife and his step-daughter, each bearing the name Jeanne, amazed him by receiving the Maid with considerable warmth, and further surprised him by growing fond of his captive. Indeed, his Aunt Jeanne, the doughty Demoiselle of Luxembourg, whose heir he hoped to become, rather complicated matters by becoming a staunch partisan of the Maid.

The prisoner could not escape, yet she was in good health and spirits, thanks to the congenial company of the three ladies and to their kind companionship. Jean of Luxembourg was well pleased on the whole; he could afford to wait while the ransom value of the Maid increased. But there were times when he was not altogether happy in mind. One afternoon, arriving at Beaurevoir, he found the three ladies of his household and the prisoner seated together on the terrace. The Demoiselle had beside her huge bowls of fruit which she was preparing for her kitchen preserving-pans; his wife and step-daughter worked together on a piece of tapestry; the Maid stitched at the fine cambric kerchiefs she was making for the Demoiselle's birthday, as if her life depended on the tiny, even stitches.

"Greetings," called Luxembourg, as he mounted the steps leading to the terrace. "With so many of one name, I needs must add greetings to you, Demoiselle, my aunt; greetings, wife; greetings, daughter; and to you, Maid, greetings." Each acknowledged his entrance in her own way—his aunt by a glance, his wife by rising to loosen his armour and fetch refreshments, his step-daughter and the Maid rose and bowed, then resumed their tasks.

"For Heaven's sake, Jean!" cried the Demoiselle, "wear the mask over your eye-socket. It gives me shivers along my spine when you stare at me with that pucker where your right eye should be. I'm sure these maids here can hardly bear to look at you. That's better. Come and sit by me and tell me what brings the Bishop—the ex-Bishop I should say—of Beauvais to Beaurevoir so often? He's over and back to Paris University; over and back to the English; over and back to Burgundy."

"Why? Has he been here today?"

"Yes, indeed. Enquired if you were here; then, when he found you gone, he rode to the Duke's quarters."

"He will not find the Duke there. Philip's cousin in the Lowlands has died suddenly—leaving no male heirs—and the Duke is gone posting to Flanders; it's likely that the duchies of Limbourg and Brabant will be his now—as well as Namur, which he gained last year."

"Much gets more," commented the Demoiselle, acidly. "Will you two girls carry these bowls of fruit to the kitchens, and make ready the copper pans and the syrups; I would not trust the serving-maids with such a task. Call me when you have all in readiness and warn the kitchen-boys to have good clear fires when I come down to watch the preserving."

The girls folded their needlework and put it away. The Demoiselle or her nephew did not speak again until Jeanne d'Arc and young Jeanne of Bar had gone away, laden with bowls of fruit.

"She still wears boy's clothing," remarked Luxembourg, his eyes following the Maid.

"Yes. We pleaded with her, offered her a woman's garb. Young Jeanne wanted her to accept a bolt of cloth, good *cramoisie* that she had by since her last visit to Arras. But the Maid would not. She said that she would have liked to do so to please the three of us—and that she would have done it for us sooner than for any three on earth—but that she was obeying a command to wear man's clothes. And that command she could not—or would not—disobey."

"You are all too easy with her. Soon she may be with those who will make her obey."

"Nephew! What do you mean? You know my views on the matter. Don't tell me that you are still negotiat-ing—selling a Christian maid, and, as far as I can judge, selling someone who is very dear to God."

"God delivered her into my hands, didn't He? They are offering good money, Aunt. Three bidders, the Uni-versity of Paris, the English, and Burgundy. After all, I am but a younger son of a younger son. I'd be a fool not to negotiate. The English are levying a tax on Normandy that should yield ten thousand *livres;* six thousand has been their highest offer up to this, but the Bishop of Beauvais told me that this tax should mean that the English will empower him to offer more."

"The Bishop of Beauvais, indeed! He's no more the Bishop of Beauvais than you are. Didn't they turn on him, both priests and people of Beauvais, and put him out of his own Cathedral? Anyway, why is he, Pierre Cauchon, meddling in the matter? Can't he let the English do their own haggling?"

"He says that he is still the Bishop of Beauvais, and that the Maid was captured within the confines of his diocese. Besides, the English have entrusted him with the business of negotiating her sale."

"I should say that the girl is between the devil and the deep sea—there is not much to choose between the English and the University, if it's before either of those tribunals she must appear. While Gerson was Chancellor of the University she would have got fair play; he seemed much impressed with her evidence at Poitiers. Now that he's dead, Paris won't give her much quarter; the University is too beholden to the Duke for that. And the English have said all along that should they get her, they'll burn her as a witch. Jean—you mustn't sell that girl. Have I not told you that Beaurevoir will go to you at my death? I'm an old woman, with not long to live. Don't disgrace the name of Luxembourg by selling the Maid."

"Demoiselle, ten thousand *livres* is a lot of money.

Think of what could be done with it, even here in Beaurevoir. Besides, they may not put her to death. They may
use her to bring Charles to his knees. The English did not
kill Charles of Orleans. How many years has he been in
prison in England? Not under rigorous restraint either, I
should say, judging by the love-songs he writes; all the
ladies of the English lords over here carry copies of his
latest sonnets."

"Charles is a Duke of the blood. The Maid is but a
peasant wench, unheard-of up till a year ago. Her parents
are obscure folk of no influence whatsoever. And she is
from the marches of Lorraine. You know the reputation
Lorraine has for sorcery and witchcraft. There would be
little to-do if one whom her enemies call a witch from
Lorraine were burnt. Who ever heard of a Duke being
burned for witchcraft?"

"I don't believe they'll harm her. Anyway, Charles the
King is bound to come to her aid."

"He's very slow about doing anything of the sort—as
far as I can see."

"He's probably collecting ransom money; or deciding
which of the towns of France to offer for her person.
'Twould be a good joke if he offered Orleans—after all
the Maid went through to deliver it."

"From what I hear, Orleans would gladly give itself
as her ransom. But there is to be no question of that.
I want you to promise me that you will not sell her. I
am not asking you to give her her freedom; but don't
sell her—to any party."

"Aunt, you ask too much. Never in my life have I

had—and I'm never likely to have again—wealth thrust upon me. I'd be a fool not to seize my chance."

"Jean, I have never craved anything of anyone, but I do now ask this one request of you. Do not refuse me— or those who have gone before us, and who, if they were here, would surely ask you not to do this deed. We Luxembourgs have in our veins the blood of kings and queens, the blood of emperors—yes, there has been a saint among our forbears. Don't disgrace the name you bear."

"I have my future to look to. Even should you leave me Beaurevoir, you know that my brother, being older, will dispute the inheritance."

"Listen, Jean. If you will agree to what I ask, I will have the notary fetched here and now, and make over not only Beaurevoir but also my entire possessions, my money, my jewels. Only promise to do as I ask."

It was the opportunity of a lifetime, and Jean of Luxembourg was a man of his age.

"When I sign such a deed, then and only then do I give my word," he said.

The Demoiselle, remarking that there was no time like the present, especially as there was the possibility of Pierre Cauchon's returning with the new offer from the English, called to a passing servitor to fetch the notary and bid him bring quills and parchment.

It was quickly done. Beaurevoir and the wealth of the aged Demoiselle passed into the keeping of her nephew. When the notary finally withdrew, the old lady handed Jean the deeds. "And now you will give me your promise," she said.

"And now I must see what the English offer. I am in a better position to bargain; thanks, Aunt, for giving me your earthly possessions. It will save me much trouble later on." And, hitching his ever-slipping mask to hide his unsightly eye-socket, Jean the one-eyed of Luxembourg went out.

The shock of the treachery of her favourite nephew, the sudden bitter realisation that she had been reduced to dependence and poverty by one so near and dear, had a numbing effect on the Demoiselle. She sat alone on the terrace, suddenly feeling very old, the frailty and infirmity of an accumulation of years all in a moment laying their constricting weight upon her bent shoulders. It seemed that she should be weeping, but no tears came; she would have liked company and consolation, but that would have meant unfolding to others who loved him the perfidy of Jean. For a long while she sat there, alone and grieving. She might have remained longer, but young Jeanne of Bar ran on to the terrace, whitefaced, breathless.

"Oh, Madame! Oh, Demoiselle! Something awful has happened."

"What is it?" (as if anything could be worse than what had just happened).

"Jeanne d'Arc, the Maid. Fallen from the high tower—whether she fell or leaped I cannot say. Oh, Demoiselle, pray that she be not mortally hurt. See, the guards are fetching her in."

The Burgundian guards were, indeed, carrying an inert form. The Demoiselle hastened towards them, the weeping Jeanne of Bar flying to fetch her mother and the *béguine* from the kitchens.

"Lay her here on these cushions," ordered the old lady, her own trouble forgotten in the face of this new tragedy. "Is she alive?"

"Yes. She moaned when we lifted her. But she must be badly injured; that tower is over sixty feet tall."

"Her heart beats. Go, fetch water and bandages; ride, one of you, to the Duke's camp and fetch the surgeon from Dijon who always travels with the Duke."

"How did it happen?" asked the quiet-voiced wife of Jean of Luxembourg, who, with the *béguine*, had hastened to the terrace. No one answered for a moment, but stood around in a ring, watching the Demoiselle trying to pour a spoonful of cordial between the clenched teeth.

"I was with her up to a moment or two ago," volunteered young Jeanne. "She was saddened when she heard the soldiers behind us on the tower talking of what was to happen to Compiègne when the Duke takes it."

"I was under the trees yonder," said one of the soldiers who had helped carry the Maid to the terrace. "I was watching the Maid as she stood looking down over the battlements. Before I could shout a warning to my fellows above, she leaped, just leaped, out into the air and fell by the edge of the moat."

"She said to me that her Voices had told her that this day she was being sold to the English. Oh, see! She's opening her eyes. She is coming to herself!" young Jeanne sobbed with relief.

Sure enough the Maid regained semi-consciousness.

She did not try to move, just opened her eyes, looked at those about her, then closed her eyes again and moaned.

"Dear child," said the Demoiselle, "take another sip of this. You are not dying, that's one thing certain." She managed to get a little more of the cordial down the girl's throat; Jeanne opened her eyes and tried to sit up.

"No. Lie there until the surgeon comes; we do not know what damage has been done, though, as far as I can make out, no limbs have been broken."

"The bonesetter is in the kitchen," the *béguine* said. "He was setting young Henri's collar-bone, you remember, the lad who fell from his horse yesterday."

"Get him here at once," cried the Demoiselle. In a few minutes the bonesetter arrived. The soldier who had fetched him had told him of the accident, so he lost no time but began flexing the Maid's arms and legs; he felt her shoulders, moved his skilled fingers up the nape of her neck and ran his hands over her head, feeling for a break or crack. There was not a bone broken, he told the Demoiselle; couldn't understand how she fell from such a height—that's if she *did* fall—without smashing her limbs like dry faggots. And, if she threw herself, the injuries would have been worse still. It was incredible.

"I have sent for the Duke's surgeon," said the Demoiselle. "She may have grievous internal wounds. It couldn't be possible to fall that height and remain unhurt."

The bonesetter shook his head. "No, Lady. She'd be bleeding by this time and bleeding heavily. Beyond being badly bruised, you'll find she'll be all right."

The Demoiselle took the basin of hot broth the

béguine had brought and began to coax the Maid to take little sips. Young Jeanne and her mother chafed her hands and feet.

"You may go back to your posts." When she had ordered the soldiers and servants away, the Demoiselle spoke softly to her two kinswomen. "She may say things when she rallies that it were not meet for any ears but ours to hear. People coming out of deep swoons like this, lay bare many things. And what we three hear we keep in confidence, as though we were her confessor and she one who knelt beside us to be shriven." The others nodded. Moments of consciousness were now becoming more frequent. Finally the Maid spoke.

"What happened?" she asked, wonderingly.

"You had a great fall, child. Lie still and do not think about it."

"I did not fall. I leaped." And tears gathered in Jeanne's eyes, tears that she had not yet the strength to raise her hand to stem. The Demoiselle wiped her eyes. "Do not weep," she said. "You are safe. God took care of you. You know what the Psalm, *Qui habitat*, says: *He hath given His angels charge over thee, to keep thee in all thy ways. In their hands they shall bear thee up, lest thou dash thy foot against a stone.* God kept you safe."

"God," repeated the Maid in a dazed manner, "God." Then she began to weep in earnest. "I have offended Him. I have sinned against the good God. Never before have I gone against the advice of my Voices; they told me not to jump; but when they warned me that soon I am to be given into the hands of the English—I was afraid. I commended myself to God and Our Lady before I leaped. Now I fear that I have sinned against God."

"Don't cry, child. If you are sorry, God has forgiven you already. He makes allowances for us that we would not even make for ourselves."

"Here is the surgeon," cried young Jeanne of Bar. With the surgeon was Jean of Luxembourg, his face set in hard, angry lines.

"See to her injuries, quickly, man," he ordered. "Go you below, and you," he told his wife and step-daughter. When they had gone, he drew the Demoiselle aside. "So. You thought to break the bargain by helping her to escape," he said, his eye-mask slipping down and making him squint malevolently.

"No, Jean. I knew nothing of it until your step-daughter ran in to tell me. I was here from the time you rode away until they carried her in and laid her there."

"Here, maybe, but with a plan hatched out that might have lost me the ten thousand *livres* Cauchon is bringing here tonight. If she had died, your life would have also been forfeit, Aunt—no longer Demoiselle of Luxembourg!"

"No injury that I can discover," remarked the surgeon, rising and approaching the knight and the old lady. "It's most remarkable. She says she jumped from the tower; well-nigh seventy feet, I would say."

"Jumped, fiddlesticks!" retorted Luxembourg; he strode to where the Maid lay, still weeping and inconsolable.

"What happened?" he demanded.

"I jumped. I sinned against God. My Voices kept saying 'Nay'—but I jumped. I became afraid of what the English may do to me."

"Trumped-up lies!" snapped the other. "The Demoiselle put you up to some way of escaping. Tied some sheets together, no doubt, and you were getting down when they gave way. You could not fall from that height without either being killed outright, or suffering serious harm. The surgeon says you are all right."

"Badly shaken, of course," put in the surgeon, "and bruised and sore all over; a few days' rest should see her as well as ever."

"Tell the truth, girl," ordered Luxembourg. "Did not the Demoiselle here urge you to this? Had she not planned an escape for you—some way of getting you back to your friends in Compiègne?"

"No, sire, no! She knew nothing of it. My Voices told me that my sale to the English was certain—that the money was even tonight being handed over; I could not bear the thought and became terrified of what God has willed for me. I jumped off the tower."

"I don't believe you," the new master of the fortress declared. "If you jumped that height without injury, it's clear proof that the witchcraft the English attribute to you is no imaginary thing, but sheer devil-dealing, nothing else. But I am inclined to think that you are lying to shield someone. However, it will not happen again. I will not let you out of my sight for the rest of your stay here—which I do not think will be very long!"

He turned on his heel. "Ring for the household women to bring her couch and coverings into the south hall," he told the surgeon. "And you, Aunt, have some wraps fetched for yourself; you also must remain with us in the south hall. I do not trust you any more than I do the Maid."

Servants hurried with lighted torches; others carried the Maid from the terrace and settled her on a trestle-bed in the hall; the Demoiselle, trembling from head to foot at the humiliation and treachery she had experienced, preceded her nephew and the surgeon, and finding a seat near a torchlight, sat quietly there. When she felt sufficiently composed, she would take her Book of Hours and read the Psalms that had comforted so many hearts, wounded like hers. The surgeon, after a short whispered conversation with Luxembourg, went away. The Lord of the Castle walked up and down, moodily, frowning each time his eye-mask slipped, which was frequently.

"Demoiselle," called the Maid. The old lady and her nephew together approached the couch.

"Please get me a priest. Friar Pasquerel—any priest. . . . I want to confess."

The Demoiselle looked at her nephew. He shook his head. "Let her wait for her shriving; hasty confessions leave little time for repentance."

"For shame, Jean! How would *you* like to be refused a priest if your heart told you that you needed shriving? Besides," she lowered her voice, "if it's true that she will be in other hands shortly, she may not have much time for confessing. Let her make her peace with God, as you hope to find similar mercy yourself. If you are, as you say, master here now, don't begin by refusing soul-comfort to one under your care. I will fetch the friar myself; send some of the guard with me if you don't trust me."

Though anger and suspicion were still strong in him, Jean allowed his aunt to summon Friar Pasquerel, who, with d'Aulon and Pierre d'Arc, was imprisoned in another wing of Beaurevoir. While the priest heard the Maid's confession, the others moved to the far end of the hall. Scarcely was the sacrament administered, than there was a clatter on the drawbridge and much noise of men and horses in the courtyard beneath.

Pierre Cauchon entered, accompanied by notaries and Burgundian and English knights.

"Is she ready?" he asked. "What's this tale of jumping from the tower? Not hurt, is she?" He seemed unwilling to approach the Maid.

"The bonesetter and the Duke's surgeon have examined her and they say there is nothing broken, no internal injuries either; only soreness and bruising that will pass in a day or two."

"We are taking her tonight."

"You are taking her three days from now, not an hour sooner." The Demoiselle would not deign to use the title *Bishop* to Cauchon. "She has had a great fright and been under much distress of soul as well. She needs rest and care before she can be moved."

"She will get rest and care where we are taking her. I took the precaution of having the men bring a litter. And the Duke's surgeon will give her all the care she needs to restore her to health. Call the bearers and see that she's made secure on the litter; we want no further attempts at escape. You, old lady, up off your knees!"—

for the Demoiselle was making a last appeal to Luxembourg—"unless you want us to take you also as a traitor; the Duke has the same law for all traitors, young or old, rich or poor, man or woman, Demoiselle or *Pucelle*. Luxembourg, here is the gold from Normandy; ten bags, with a thousand *livres* in each. Have your treasurer count the money at once and give me a receipt for it; I'll write you a receipt for the prisoner."

The clink, clink of the money being counted and the murmur of the treasurer and his assistants filled the otherwise silent hall. Then, with tears running down their faces, the ladies of Luxembourg bade farewell to the Maid. She, still not fully recovered from the shock, physical and mental, of her fall, tried to concentrate on what was happening. The few months in this fortress had been happy ones; now she was going forth again to live among fighting men; only this time they were not her own soldiers nor those of her King; they were the enemy. In her army the gentle manners of Alençon, the nobility of le Bâtard, the faithfulness of d'Aulon, the sanctity of Friar Pasquerel, had raised, as it were, invisible walls about her; within those walls her virtue, like a tall tower, could be safe and unassailable. Now the tower stood alone, without moat or rampart. But there was always God—God, Whom she had offended only a little while ago. This was a way in which to prove to Him how truly grieved she was for what she had done. She would accept her imprisonment by the English as an atonement; she would show neither fear nor distress. When they jolted her on that litter she would not cry out, but would remember the pain Our Lord had endured on His terrible journey up the hill of Calvary.

"I am ready," she said; and those who had seen her in tears up till a few minutes before, wondered at her serenity.

"Shameless sight!" said Cauchon. "A wench dressed like a man."

"Are you sure you would not like that length of cloth?" whispered Jean of Luxembourg's wife, "or one of my young Jeanne's gowns?"

"Nay, I dare not—now. I must obey all my Lord's commands from this on; besides, a woman living among men is safer dressed as a man."

"What muttering goes on?" asked Cauchon. "Ah! Money counted and right, eh? Ten thousand *livres*, Luxembourg. Not every Maid fetches so high a price. Take your weeping ladies to Arras tomorrow and buy them fairings to console them for the loss of their guest. Captains, make an escort. I myself will ride beside the litter. Come on, fellows, we are awaited up the river."

Jean of Luxembourg did not accompany them outside the hall. He was loth to leave the ten heavy bags guarded by the treasurer. Well, a good riddance! There had been a time when he himself went in hourly dread of being seized as a hostage by the King's men—a hostage until his prisoner was handed over. There had been days and nights when negotiations did not go to his liking, when it seemed doubtful that he would get his money at all; times, too, when the fact that he was Burgundy's vassal and, at the same time, a mercenary in the pay of the English, made him fear that either of his over-lords would step in and take by force what was his by capture. All had gone, in the end, far better than he had either anticipated or hoped for. The master-stroke of strategy was, of course, getting old Aunt Jeanne to ensure his inheritance; near the end of her tether anyway—she looked older than her eighty years tonight—just as well have things right before his brother got at her in her dotage and persuaded her to have him, the elder of the two, nominated Count of Luxembourg. She would have remembered that quarrel they had some years previously, the time he, Jean, had made an example of a prisoner. Broken parole, had the knave, and the captive's mother had thought to ransom her son with six thousand crowns. Having sent the money, she thought Jean of Luxembourg fool enough to send her boy back to where she sat in her doorway, waiting. Her son came back, yes, but only his head, which he, Luxembourg himself, had carried on his spear right up to the good wife and dropped in her lap. His aunt had always held that little matter against him. It was just as well that he had made sure of Beaurevoir and all that went with it. . . .

These pleasant musings filled his mind until the torches of the party faded away into the darkness. Then he turned from the window to note, with some surprise, that the ladies of his house had, all three, left the south hall. Sulking, by God! Well, let them to it. That old one had not long to live; young Jeanne of Bar would be betrothed before Christmas, whether she would or no; and his wife had better learn more pleasant manners towards her lord and master, and that soon, otherwise she would have to be taught.

Chapter Twelve

I SABEL D'ARC had good neighbors. Now that Jacquemin was married and gone from his father's house, and the boy-knights—whom their mother had not seen since they left Domrémy—were, one at court, one in prison, and Jacques d'Arc on his sick-bed, the neighbours in Domrémy helped Isabel with her farming and gardening. The girls who had grown up with the Maid, slipped in and lent a hand with the spinning, with the dairy work, with the housework. The men who had so much enjoyed Jacques' company in the long summer evenings when they had lounged on the grass patch outside his door, watching the passers-by on the Langres road, now took turns sitting up nights with the sick man. It was not likely that he would see another harvest; when vintage time came, Isabel would not need to scold him for his rowdy returnings, for helping—too assiduously—to sample new wine. The women sat with Isabel, brought possets of whey for Jacques, or a pillow stuffed with fresh herbs to refresh the invalid and make wholesome the air in the sick-room.

No one referred to the subject uppermost in every mind. They knew that it was sheer misery and worry over his daughter—how he had doted on her!—which had reduced the vital and gay Jacques d'Arc to a gaunt shadow of a man, who grew daily more morose and dull in himself. Not a good sign, Jean Morel told Isabel. This was the kind of wasting sickness where, as debility of the body grew more and more noticeable, so too the flame of reason dulled and dimmed and finally flickered out.

Even to Isabel no one mentioned her daughter. The neighbours knew how Isabel had felt all along; she was almost the only one in Domrémy who seemed to sense that the adventure could come to no good end. When everyone else was wild with excitement and spent the day gossiping over the news from Orleans or from Rheims, Isabel had been hoeing her garden, or tossing her hay, or thinning her beans. Once or twice, when the excitement was at its height, she had slipped away on some pilgrimage or other; every Saturday saw her at Bermont shrine, praying before the statue of the Blessed Virgin. How often in former years the Domrémy women had heard her scold Jeanne and Catherine for leaving their tasks in the fields to make the little pilgrimage to Bermont; now she seemed to have taken it on herself to keep up the practice her daughters—one dead and one who would be better off dead—had begun.

Despite the fact that her husband was a very sick man, no one in Domrémy was surprised when, around Passiontide, Isabel d'Arc got ready to go on yet another pilgrimage to Le Puy. She had gone there before for the great double feast of the Annunciation and the Incarnation; that was two years agone when the feasts had fallen on a Good Friday and when her daughter had ridden to relieve Orleans. Her son Jacquemin, and a childless couple from Domrémy, had accompanied her that year. They had said, on their return, that could Orleans be relieved by prayer, Isabel d'Arc might well claim to have raised the siege. It was the biggest pilgrimage ever seen at Puy-en-Velay; a quarter of a million people came there in that fateful spring of 1429. Not only could one hear the dialects of every province in France, but Germans, Italians, Spaniards and Swedes mingled in the throng; pilgrims from places as far apart as the isles of Greece in the east and the island of Ireland in the west came barefoot to the Great Pardon, when three of the greatest feasts of the Christian year coincided. Thirty-three people were killed in the crush. But Isabel d'Arc feared neither the press in the crowd nor the dizzy climb up the Corneille rock which was part of the penitential exercises undertaken by the pilgrims.

At the Great Pardon that March, the four from Domrémy had met a poor friar, also intent on doing his devotions and gaining the indulgences granted to those who visited Notre Dame de Puy. He had told them that he was there as the ambassador of the girl they called the Maid, she whom Charles and his party hoped that God had sent to deliver Orleans. He himself was attached to the Maid's household, being her confessor; she had wanted to make this pilgrimage, but as her presence was sorely needed elsewhere—some of the court all for having her as a leader, some totally opposed to her—he, Friar Pasquerel, had promised to come in her stead. That was why he was endeavouring to perform the holy exercises with all possible devotion—he was trying to do the pilgrimage as the Maid would have done it; she always put her whole heart into her prayers.

When they told him who they were, the Friar was overjoyed. He and Isabel d'Arc had had long conversations before they parted—he for the court, she for Domrémy.

Now that far graver troubles menaced her daughter, it was natural that, in 1431, Isabel should again go to Puy for Lady Day. Her cousin Laxart and his wife and child drove their live-stock from Burey-le-Petit to Domrémy and undertook to look after everything in Isabel's absence. They could be counted upon to give special care to poor Jacques, who lay in a stupor, seemingly unaware of what went on all around him.

So she set off on the eve of the feast of St. Patrick of Ireland, walking her ten leagues a day, come wet, come fine, come wind, come calm. First she kept to the highroad—the Langres road, paddling along barefoot to Langres and Dijon, a three days' journey. Although Dijon was in Burgundian territory, no pilgrim from loyalist France ever felt fear, for all pilgrims to Puy-en-Velay got safe conduct from every king and ruler in Christendom. From Dijon to the great abbey of Citeaux, where she got a good night's rest and was well-provisioned for the rest of her journey; on to Beaune and Chalon-sur-Saone; then she followed the river for a day and came to Cluny, where the monks ministered to the

wants of the many pilgrims making for le Puy. On by
the Saone to Lyons, where she joined a confraternity
that was setting out, first going west on foot until they
met the Loire at Feurs and then following the river
southwards until, on the tenth day after leaving Domrémy, on the very day of the feast, she reached le Puy.

Not waiting to enter the hostels to have her sore feet
attended to, or to seek a meal from the almoners of
Notre Dame de Puy, Isabel d'Arc proceeded to hear
Mass and receive Holy Communion; then she did the
penitential stations, fasting. Pausing only to take a drink
of water, she assisted at several Masses. It was high noon
before she gave herself time to eat. No one from Domrémy was with her. Having eaten and rested, she went
through the crowds hoping against hope that she might
meet the Friar who had been her daughter's confessor.
Failing to see anyone resembling him, she resumed her
devotions, this time praying for her husband, com-
mending his recovery or happy death—whichever God
willed—to the merciful Mother.

The confraternity from Lyons had told her that they
hoped to get a boat which would take them as far as
Feurs on the return journey. They would rest until midnight and set out then; the moon was almost full and it
would be easy travelling; she could have a seat if she
wished. They did not know who she was; they had
not noticed her tears when one of the priests who had
travelled with them reminded them of the prayers being
said throughout Dauphiny for the Maid's deliverance;
they had not remarked upon her inability to join in
repeating the Collects after the priests, as all of those

about her were doing. Every word they uttered smote her heart. . . . *"Who hast permitted the Maid to be cast into prison as she laboured to obey Thy holy commands. . . ." ". . . Grant that she may be delivered from their power unhurt, and finally accomplish the work which Thou hast commanded her. . . ." ". . . Break in pieces the fetters of the Maid . . . who now by our enemies is held in prison. . . ." ". . . May she go forth unhurt. . . ." ". . . Through Jesus Christ our Lord. Amen."*

Her grief and weariness weighed heavily upon her. Finally she withdrew from the crowds and sat apart, resting before beginning the long journey home, allowing her sorrow the unusual—for her—luxury of tears and sighs. The first five decades of her life had passed by calmly enough, she reflected, looking back over the past. It was the last couple of years that had brought the heaviest trials. Her life had been a hard one; unremitting toil had calloused her hands and bowed her shoulders. She had known the losses that are the common lot of those who live on the land—all the calves dying one summer, several sheep lost during a bitter winter, a young horse destroyed in a lightning storm, hay and crops carried away when the Meuse had flooded their valley. She had experienced the added miseries of Burgundian and bandit raids, when some of the farm buildings and their ricks of straw and hay went up in flames. On one such occasion she had had to seek refuge for herself and her family in a house owned by a woman of doubtful reputation—glad of any shelter when flight from the greater dangers in Domrémy became imperative.

But the last few years had brought trials far greater than any of those. There had been Catherine's death; then, the following year, Jeanne's flight; a few months after that Jean and Pierre departed; the previous fall Jacques had taken ill—Jeanne's capture seemed to unman him, he was never the same since word came that she had finally been handed over to the English. Jacquemin had married and left Domrémy. In three short years, Isabel d'Arc's family had left their home; she had become widowed and childless while yet her husband and children lived; all that remained were her prayers and her memories:

> *Her brood gone from her*
> *And her thoughts still*
> *As waters under*
> *A ruined mill.*

Hastily plucking her thoughts from herself—she never had wasted her time in self-pity—the mother thought of Jeanne. How were things with her girl, she wondered? What would they do with her when this farce of a trial was over? There was only one outcome when one was found guilty in a trial for witchcraft; Isabel was not ignorant of the law in that matter. She remembered a day not so many years past when she had been to the great fair in Nancy; one of the attractions had been a witch-burning. Isabel had gone, with the other Domrémy men and women, to witness the sight. It had an element of danger that attracted sight-seers; the witch might fix her evil eye on some unlucky soul who instantly lost his wits or, perhaps, became possessed himself by the fiend that had, up till her death, made of the witch his human dwelling-place. Some never dared to look up at the stake at all; others crossed themselves devoutly before doing so; Isabel had been unable to bear the screams of the condemned when they set fire to the faggots beneath her feet, and had fled from the scene, fingers in her ears. Across the years she still could hear those screams. Would Jeanne, flesh of her flesh and bone of her bone, utter screams like that? Would they set the hungry fire to eat the soft flesh from her straight young limbs? The mother in her moaned, but the Christian in her prayed. Better scream in a fire that did its work terribly but quickly, than suffer forever in a fire that never consumed though it gnawed eternally at the imperishable soul.

She hardly noticed the three who had seated themselves nearby, until scraps of their conversation began to make an impact on her mind, gradually freeing itself from the uninterrupted preoccupation with grief and care. There was a noble and his lady, both very richly dressed and wearing the colours of Orleans. The man bore insignia that showed he was some personage of high standing, some official of the court, perhaps, some grandee in charge of one or other of the Duke's estates or *châteaux*. Isabel had noticed them earlier in the day and had been struck by the intent, devout manner in which they performed the penitential exercises. With them was a youth, some young son of a noble house, his family crest embroidered on his tunic—Isabel, herself an excellent needlewoman, could not help but notice the

fine needlework. The three were serious, deeply perturbed; they talked together in low, urgent tones.

"How many days has the trial lasted, up till now?"

"Over forty days come last Monday. They sit every
day except Sunday."

"No word from the King?"

"Never a word."

"Is she allowed any comfort in her imprisonment?"

"Comfort! The poor lass is chained by the hands and
feet to a post. English *houcepaillers* guard her all the
time. At night they pass a chain around her body and
padlock it securely to one of the rafters. The only thing
they've spared her is confinement in the iron cage."

"Has she any women about her?" It was the lady who
asked this question. Isabel, now alert, listened anxiously
for the answer.

"No. She has asked again and again to be taken to the
Church prisons and put in care of women guards——"

"She *should* be in the Church prison. Is she not being
tried by a Church court?"

"Yes, but as you know well, good Boucher, Cauchon
has the ordering of everything concerning the trial and
the prisoner."

"He never forgave her since that time last year when
Beauvais declared for the King and drove him out. He
swore vengeance on the Maid."

The peasant woman sitting a little way from them had
drawn near; unsure of her reception by such grand folk,
but emboldened by her need to know all they knew, she
bowed to the trio:

"I heard what you said—about the Maid. I came all the

way from Domrémy to make the pilgrimage for her——"

"From Domrémy! Good woman, come and sit by us. Did you know her as a child?"

"Yes, Sire. Yes, Madame." (Yes, I knew her since that Epiphany night when the women first laid her, tiny and helpless, in my arms.)

"What is it you would know? You do know, of course, that she is imprisoned in Rouen and standing her trial. They sent even to Domrémy, 'tis said, to gather proof that she's a witch."

"Yes. They were questioning the children and the neighbours. They did not come to me. But please, Messires, Madame, tell me how goes it with her?"

"Badly. Not but that she gives a good account of herself; she answers their questions as though 'twere given her from above what to say. But they had her judged before they began."

"You met her?"

"Yes," the young knight spoke; "I rode with her in the wars last year. Messer Boucher, here—the Treasurer of the Duke of Orleans—and his good lady, they had her to stay with them as guest when she was in Orleans the time of the siege; and again a year ago, when she visited the city. The Maid loved Orleans and all Orleans loved her."

"She stayed with you?"

"She did, indeed," said Madame Boucher; "we loved her as a daughter. We have come to do the pilgrimage for her deliverance from her enemies."

"You don't think then that she's a witch—or a

heretic—or a loose woman, as some—even among our own side—say?"

"Heavens, no, woman! It's a sacrilege, to my mind, even to think or say the like. The girl was good through and through; and devoted to Our Lady and the saints. Not a morning while she stayed with us in Orleans but she rose at dawn to pray and prepare herself for Mass and Holy Communion."

"Thank God! I knew my Jeanne was good—but——"

"*Your* Jeanne! You are——"

"Yes. Her mother, lady."

The two men sprang up from the ground where they were seated, and bowed deeply; Madame Boucher flung her arms wide and wept with the peasant woman as she embraced her. For a few moments all were silent.

"She took a house for you in Orleans, you know, a lease of a house near the church, where she arranged that you are to come to live in your old age, should you be left alone in Domrémy."

"I must go," said Isabel d'Arc. "The pilgrims from Lyons will be waiting for me. The moon is rising."

"Our carriage waits at Clermont-Ferrand. If you would travel with us as far as there, we shall be pleased to send you home in comfort. We can easily hire a carriage to take us back to Orleans."

"Thank you, Messires, and you, Madame, but I would like to return the hard way; it is for Jeanne—and my husband, too, who is like to die with the sickness that came on him since he heard the bad news last fall——"

"Let us, at least, convey you to where the pilgrims from Lyons are assembling."

"I have not told them anything of what I told you. They would wonder at seeing me in such fine company. Better that I go as I came. It has given me great happiness to speak with you and to know that you believe that Jeanne is a good maid."

"Will you accept——" Jacques Boucher hastily replaced the purse he had proffered, when he saw that money was the last thing the Maid's mother would take from him.

"No, Sire. I have had what I value more than gold—word of my daughter. And the surety that she has good friends who believe in her—no matter how the trial ends."

"Is there nothing we can do?" asked Madame Boucher.

"Just to keep on praying, Madame. Jeanne will need all the prayers she can get, poor child. Tell the people of Orleans not to fail her now or when the trial ends."

Bowing again, Isabel went towards the church to make a last visit before joining the home-bound pilgrims. They set off at midnight, their *Salve Regina* sounding sweetly along the Loire as they bade farewell to the Black Virgin of Puy.

The Domrémy woman covered the road faster on the return journey, reaching Citeaux for the ceremony of the washing of the feet on Holy Thursday. It was Easter Saturday evening when she reached home. The kindly gentlefolk from Orleans had said that from Holy Thursday until the Saturday after Easter there would be no sessions of the tribunal before which her daughter had to appear. That, in itself, was a good thing. It gave time. And time might yet bring Charles with a ransom, or some of the good captains of France riding to the defeat of the English in Rouen and the rescue of the Maid. But it might be worse for Jeanne within the prison walls than facing the judges. Chained hands and feet, the young knight had said; and with no woman in her company. . . . Probably with brutal guards often soused in ale. As she walked the last league home, Isabel d'Arc, unmindful of her own aching, bleeding feet, but in anguish for her child, reminded the Mother of God that she, too, knew what it was to have a Child in prison at the mercy of gaolers; she would surely protect the Maid.

All was unchanged in her home in Domrémy; Jacques d'Arc no better—no worse. The Laxarts were glad to see her; they wished to spend Easter in their own home, and left shortly after her arrival. The neighbours came in, one by one, when they heard that Isabel had returned, anxious to hear how she had fared. She told no one of her encounter with the Treasurer of Orleans. The callers had plenty to relate, however, of things that had happened in her absence. For, on Monday of Holy Week, a train of merchants had chanced by, merchants from some Lowland town, returning from Normandy with supplies of cider and other commodities. They had been in Rouen and had much to say about the Maid and the trial. One swore that if ever there was a trial noted for unfairness, this was it. The two judges were Pierre Cauchon and Jean Lemaistre of the Inquisition. Lemaistre, indeed, showed that he seemed ill at ease in his position, but he was overruled by Cauchon. Once or twice he tried to withdraw, but having been threatened, he yielded; others also, honourable and fair-minded men, who had de-

murred, the merchants said, at the unfairness of the proceedings, felt the weight of Cauchon's displeasure. One,
La Fontaine, who was suspected of having gone to see
Jeanne to give her certain advice about her answers, had
to leave Rouen in haste and under cover of darkness.
Another, de Houppeville, was thrown into prison for
saying that, in his opinion, the proceedings were invalid,
as Cauchon was going against his immediate superior and
Metropolitan, the Archbishop of Rheims, who had pre-
sided at the Poitiers commission that, in 1429, had declared the Maid to be in good faith. When the rumour
got about next day that, for his criticism of the trial
judge, poor Houppeville had found himself a prisoner,
there was some murmuring among a section of the forty
Bishops and University Doctors and Abbots who had
been summoned to sit on the tribunal, for de Houppeville was a good man, and his word counted with many.
Whereat Cauchon made reference to the remarks anent
his own obligation to abide by the Archbishop of
Rheims' ruling, and added: "If the Archbishop is still of
the same mind as he was at Poitiers, why is he not here
to defend and uphold this impostor Maid? His very
absence is in itself proof that he has changed his mind
concerning her." Another of those summoned to sit on
the tribunal—the great Doctor of Law, Lohier—at the
opening of the trial declared the proceedings to be a
travesty of justice. Later, hearing that he himself was to
be sewn into a sack and thrown into the Seine, he fled
Rouen; and in a few days he was obliged to leave France
and seek sanctuary in Rome.

"Did they say anything of how my child answers all

they charge her with?" asked Isabel, as soon as a lull came in the conversation.

Yes. Some of the preachers and doctors, listening to her ready and clever answers, had said that they never heard one so young answer with such wisdom; and two averred that she was inspired by the Holy Spirit. So the merchants said.

But when it was found by the English and Cauchon that there were many on the tribunal who were growing to esteem the accused girl, a new plan had been adopted. Instead of being brought before the full court, she was now being left in her cell, and a small body of men, known to be close adherents of Cauchon, went with him to the prison each day and interrogated her there. The full tribunal would not be called upon again, the Flemish merchants said, until Cauchon had made his case unbeatable.

But her answers! Isabel might well be proud of such a daughter! One asked her: "What revelations had you from your Voices concerning your King?" And she had answered: "Send for him and he will tell you." And another had taken her up sharply on one of her answers, asking her if she were in the state of grace. "If I am not, God bring me to His grace; if I am, I pray Him keep me so." And two English squires present in the castle-hall had raised a cheer for her on a day when someone asked her about her Saints, Catherine and Margaret, to know if these holy ones hated the English. She astonished everyone when she said: "They love whom Our Lord loves; and whom He hates they hate." And there were all kinds of questions about Domrémy—their Domrémy! Isabel

would surely remember the men who had come to the
village, questioning everyone but herself, some months
agone? They asked Jeanne about the Fairy Tree, where
the children went every Lætare Sunday to sing and
dance and hold festival. They asked about the Bois
Chenu; they asked her if she had not dug up a mandrake
and kept it about her person; they asked her about the
ring her mother sent her. They said that she was known
to have been in the habit of dropping molten wax on
the heads of children and that she divined the future
of the children by this means. This and other like ac-
cusations—all preposterous, as Isabel and the Domrémy
people knew—the girl had denied vehemently.

"Did the merchants say how she was in health?"

"They said that she looked well, but pale—as one
might expect after her long term in prison. Of course,
since the public sittings were abandoned in favour of the
private interrogation in her cell, no one sees her, but
there were rumours that she was not very well early in
March. The English lords, Stafford and Warwick, sent
for the best physicians to attend her."

"Not for love of my girl," observed Isabel. "They
hope to burn her in the end and would save her for the
flames."

"Warwick would not have the doctors bleed her, so
great was his fear that she might bleed too much and die
of want of blood."

So the talk went on; it took many days before Isabel
heard all that the Flemish merchants had said. Jacques
seemed to shrink more and more into himself; there were
days when one found it hard to say whether he lived or

not. There were nights when Isabel knelt by his pallet, saying the Psalter for the dying, wondering if the neighbour who was supposed to be watching with her had fallen asleep in the chimney corner. There were a few nights when—while the weary woman rested—other watchers recited the litanies and prayers, sprinkled holy water about the sick man, held the blessed candle in his hand and the crucifix before his glazing eyes. Even as sleep overcame Isabel, her lips murmured the names over and over again, the names of all who had once surrounded her by her hearthstone. But two names were nearest her lips and heart when the curtains of unconsciousness closed over her—Jacques and Jeanne.

Chapter Thirteen

Lᴇɴᴛ ʜᴀᴅ come and gone. The Maid had fasted, as always. In prison it was harder to make this an act of real sacrifice. The one repast she allowed herself was so unpalatable, so filthily served, that it was no deprivation to forego it. If she had been asked what she missed most during those long months, she would have found it hard to decide between fresh air and the means of personal cleanliness. Seldom, if ever, during her nineteen years had she spent many daylight hours indoors; always she had had a veritable passion for washing. How often in Domrémy had her mother expostulated at the too-frequent times Jeanne was to be found down by the flat stones near the bridge, beetling her linen vigorously. "No flax growing could give linen that would stand up to all that washing," Isabel d'Arc used to say. Later, when out with the army, it was a joy to slip away to some unfrequented spot and bathe in the Loire or one of its tributaries.

Water, air, earth, fire—the four elements had always appealed to her. God seemed to permeate them. Water cleansed, refreshed, dissolved, cooled; sent the sweet sap driving up through plant and tree, making bare boughs and sere grass green and lush. It was poured in Baptism, cleansing the spirit, sending the sap of the Christian life coursing through the young soul. The Lord had changed it into wine at Galilee; He had walked on it with His blessed feet; had it issue from His riven side, together with His Blood. In the Mass the priest added it to the as yet unconsecrated wine, even as the Christian people united themselves with Him Who vouchsafed to participate in frail human nature. Once she had heard Friar Pasquerel speak of the Samaritan woman at the well where Jesus rested; the one to whom He had spoken of living water—fountains that sprang up in the souls of all who asked for it—water that assuaged the thirsts of the spirit.

On days when the fetid cell seemed more oppressive than usual, her mind longed for space, for great draughts of the heady wind of the Vosges foothills, for the tree-scented air of the Bois Chenu, for the breeze in her mother's garden, fragrant with scent of herb and flowers. She recalled her first sight of the sea and how her nostrils had expanded to fill her lungs to the uttermost with the—to her—unfamiliar air. That had been at Crotoy when they fetched her from Luxembourg's tower to Rouen. She had come by many seaport towns, by St. Valery and Eu and Dieppe; at Drugy the monks had come with their abbot and almoner to attend upon her; at Saint Riquier the citizens came with their mayor; at

Crotoy a barge was anchored, laden with the ladies of Abbeville, who wept to see her in chains, unkempt and unwashed, and had promised to pray for her. But her keenest memory of that last journey in the open was not the stopping-places or the people met en route, but the great stretch of tossing waters and the clean wind that came in from the sea. Surely God was in the air that we breathed; He lived in us and we in Him. Our souls breathed Him as surely as our lungs breathed air; His Spirit came in a rushing wind, blowing the debris and the rubbish away; His Voice came on the still air of evening when those who listened might hear.

In her prison she saw neither earth nor fire; and in any case, she had never felt the same affection for these two elements, nor did their significance seem to find parallels in her spiritual life as did the much-missed air and water.

It was hard to keep count of time. Sundays one knew by the many church bells; and the court did not sit on holydays. But there were not many feasts in April and May; except for Whit, which was Sunday, there would only be Ascension Day and the new feast of Corpus Christi, the *Fête Dieu*. It was not really so very new, but it had not been a recognized feast when Jacques and Isabel d'Arc were young. It would be consoling if those who kept her in this prison were to give her permission to receive Holy Communion and attend Mass on that day. All along she had asked, again and again, for leave to attend Mass and receive Our Lord; but they said that, being under suspicion of heresy, she was debarred from the sacraments.

Massieu, a priest of Rouen, who had been appointed

clerk to the Prosecutor, was charged with the duty of conveying the prisoner from her cell to the Chapel Royal, where the court had sat during the early days of the trial. On their way they passed a small side-chapel, and she had asked if the Blessed Sacrament were kept there. On being told that It was, she had asked Massieu if she might pause in the doorway and pray. It was little to ask, especially as her request to be allowed to hear Mass had been refused on the first day of the trial. Massieu had allowed her to stop and pray. Then, one morning, the Prosecutor, d'Estivet, chanced to come along and found Massieu and the guards waiting while Jeanne knelt looking into the chapel towards the altar where Our Lord was. The Prosecutor was furious. "I had heard of this," he told Massieu; "now I see it for myself. How dare you, rogue, let that heretic, that wanton woman, that creature fit for excommunication, approach near the holy altar of the Lord? Believe me, should you do it again, I will have you placed in prison, in such a tower that you will not know when it's sunlight or moonlight, for a month." But, despite the threats, Massieu continued to allow her to pause for a few moments every time they passed the chapel. Until the morning when d'Estivet stood there, watching to see if his previous orders were being obeyed. From that moment Jeanne lost that consolation, being hurriedly hustled past the chapel, the doors of which were kept closed. Soon after that, they decided to hold the interrogations in the prisoner's cell.

During the day-time she was wearied with the coming and going in her cell; the questioners would hardly be gone when sight-seers would come, friends of Warwick or Stafford, the great English Lords. One day Jean of Luxembourg arrived, with him that young Lacy who so often had tried to take her in his arms and make free with her on his visits to Beaurevoir Tower. The Duchess of Bedford came, own sister to Philip of Burgundy, a gentle lady who tried to persuade Jeanne to wear woman's clothes. Even though her request was ungranted, she had obtained for the captive certain things she sorely needed—clean linen, water and washing-balls. With her own hands this lady combed, washed and dried the matted hair, and had, for all her gentleness, been greatly incensed not only with the guards, but with her husband, Bedford, and the two Lords, Warwick and Stafford, for the state in which she had found the Maid. Ever since the first visit of the Duchess, there had been clean linen and towels and fresh rain-water for washing. The good lady had sent her own tailor, in the hope that Jeanne might—at the sight of the fine cloths and sample dresses from her own wardrobe—agree to have a dress made. His orders were that, if the prisoner still refused, he was not to insist but to see if he could provide her with another suit, similar to that which she wore. He never got that far, as the temptation of a defenceless girl alone in her cell was too much for him, and he tried to make the most of the opportunity; but the Maid had dealt with his like before—and now she used her firm palms and clenched fists to good purpose. While the guards were laughing and jeering at the routed tailor, the Duchess arrived to see if the dresses had been fitted.

"Why are you not about the business you were sent on?" she asked the tailor. "Get to your task, at once."

"Not in there again, Madame. Not near that she-devil."

"So. That's how you went about your errand. Serves you right if she boxed your ears." The Duchess went alone into the narrow, airless cell where the girl spent the sunny days of May. She found the prisoner in tears.

"Forget about it," she advised tersely. "I should not have trusted him to come alone. How are you? Are you in need of anything special?"

"Nothing, Madame. You are very kind."

"My dear child, I am not coming as a visitor today. I have been sent here—on a most unpleasant errand."

"Not to tell me the trial is over? I am to be put to death?"

"No. Somehow, I might have found that easier. The court has made an order that you are to be examined—as those other ladies examined you in Poitiers last year."

"I will not mind too much, if you are to be the one who will examine me."

"I will be here; in fact, it is better that we get it over and done with now. There are other matrons waiting outside. I will bring them in and let what has to be done be done quickly."

The matrons of Rouen, more intimidated by being in the company of so great a lady as the Duchess, than by being admitted to the cell of the Maid, were as brief about their business as the Duchess had asked them to be. It was true, the girl *was* a maid. It might be as well if the Duchess's own physician corroborated that, but he could not say any different from what they affirmed. Whatever else the court might find against Jeanne d'Arc, they could not say that she had surrendered her maidenhood.

The days dragged by; sometimes she wished there were fewer comings and goings in her cell. There were days when she dozed a little even while they questioned her. Cauchon and the others thought it just another bit of impudence, but they knew little of the wakeful nights when she dared not let herself sleep for fear of the guards who seemed to grow ever bolder. More than once she begged to be sent to a Church prison, where there would be women to guard her. Once Massieu had remarked on her tear-stained face and a great weal across one cheek. That was the day he had come to say that the court had said she might be given permission to hear Mass if she resumed woman's dress. "I cannot do so," she said. "I am ordered from above to wear these garments. Besides——" and her eloquent glance towards the guards told Massieu the rest. Though a priest whose life was far from virtuous in the matter of chastity, he felt shamed that the Maid—whom he knew to be holy and pure— should be forced to fight for her virtue, and with such ruffians as the English gaolers.

Her most welcome visitor was Pierre Cusquel, a workman of Rouen, who was frequently sent for to attend to the various little repairs that became necessary, either to the cell itself, or to the benches where the interrogators used to sit, or the chains that were forever either weakening somewhere or marking her body or her hands or ankles. He never spoke of the trial, except once, when he warned her to have a care how she answered, seeing that her life depended on the words she used.

"You are so young," he said, "you need someone to

advise you. Those smart answers, now—they are all right in their way, but not so good when made to the wrong men."

"Pierre, do you know what my Voices said to me when first I was captured? I had been grumbling that so ignorant a girl as I would be unable to answer the questions of learned and clever men, and the blessed saints told me not to think about it, that, in the day of such ordeal, Another would be with me and would speak for me. And it's true. When I remember each evening what I have been asked and the answers that immediately rushed to my lips, I see how right my Voices were."

"Just the same, have a care, have a care. Cauchon is a dangerous man to offend; so are some of the others; the rest are all afraid of either the English or Cauchon or both."

"What a crowd of them there was at the beginning, when I was taken to the Chapel Royal each day."

"Crowd! Nothing to what there should have been! Cauchon summoned well nigh eight score to sit on the tribunal, and only forty came."

"None from France?"

"No. None from King Charles' France. But don't fret over that. The French may have other ideas. They say that Gilles de Rais and La Hire—captains who are, no doubt, well-known to you—are daily adding to their forces in Louviers, not twenty miles from here."

What news! But the Voices had spoken to her almost daily since Easter and they spoke not of deliverance but of sufferings. In the second week of Lent they had told her not to heed the sufferings that would bring her to

Paradise; and that within three months she should be free. She had counted the moons since then. A new moon on the Tuesday after Lætare Sunday; a new moon on the Thursday after Low Sunday; a new moon on Friday—the day after Ascension Day; this was the third month. Perhaps the Voices meant that she would be set free; perhaps La Hire and the captains would ride; maybe the King was sending her ransom; perhaps they were exchanging her for Talbot or some other important prisoner in French hands. But as quickly as hope rose in her it fell again; in her heart she knew that the Voices had not meant escape.

Pierre chatted and joked. He was sorry for the girl. She was a good soul and he himself had daughters of the same age. Besides, he knew that something was afoot to bring matters to a climax. He had orders to go on to the cemetery of St. Ouen when his morning's work in the prison was done; there were platforms to be erected speedily. He wondered, as he left the prison for the urgent task at St. Ouen, if he would ever see her again.

He had hardly gone when the interrogators, headed by Cauchon, entered the cell. Today, the Wednesday of Whit week, they seemed in a different mood. Pierre Maurice, a Canon of Rouen, who had more than once spoken kindly to her during the trial, explained to her that the University of Paris had come to a decision regarding her. He would read to her what they had found, simplifying the learned and legal language so that she could follow clearly and understand what it gravely behoved her to understand. He began, stopping every now and again to see if she comprehended fully. The

University found that her visions were of Hell—not proven by texts of Scripture or by miracle; they found that the accused did not pray to God devoutly to ascertain the truth; neither did she have recourse to any learned prelate for advice; she disobeyed the Church. Here Jeanne started up to remind all that she had asked to be sent to the Pope but that no heed was taken of her request. Looking around at the group, she knew that her protests would fall on deaf ears; it were wiser to keep silence. Pierre Maurice went on and on, finally begging her to submit and confess that she had been in error; only by a humble submission could she hope to save her soul and—he greatly feared—her body, too, from destruction. All wanted to hear what she had to say.

"If I were at the judgment place and saw the brand lit and the faggots ready and I in the centre when the executioner set all alight, I would still hold to what I have said and done—as told you at the trial."

"Is that your final word?" asked Cauchon, rising.

"I have no more to say."

She lay still as their footsteps died away on the stone stairs. Slowly the implications of the final questions and her own answers dawned upon her. Truly, Heaven spoke for her. She herself, the little Domrémy girl, would have fain wept and begged for mercy; but it was given to her to act and speak with a bravery she did not feel. Ever since the first time the Voices had spoken in Domrémy, urging her on to courses of action she never, in wildest dreams, would have thought of embarking on—ever since she had first begun to go forward and obey, there had been waiting for her this aid from above. When she had said that she could not even ride to

Chinon, much less meet the great ones there, she had been told to go, and with each difficulty, the grace of meeting it would come. And so it had happened. Who had helped her ride out into the heart of France with only four strangers for company—men-at-arms who by all accounts were not men to whom her father, Jacques d'Arc, would have entrusted his daughter? Her Heavenly Father had entrusted her to their care, and she had been well looked after. Who had helped her recognise the Dauphin at Chinon? Who had told her how to answer at Poitiers, and again at Rouen? Who had given her the heart of a warrior at Orleans and the strength of a giant in the battles of the Loire campaign? Who had consoled her in the disillusionments and detachments her heart had had to learn? Who had preserved her and forgiven her when, in a moment of panic, she had thrown herself from the tower at Beaurevoir? Who saved her on the nights when the drunken gaolers struggled with her, making them reel away, muttering? He Who had given His grace at every turn of her road would not fail to give it now.

She steeled herself to look unflinchingly at the prospect of death. Although she had spoken boldly, just a few minutes before, of burning, she did not think she would meet her end in that manner. The English way was to sew one in a sack, attach many weights, and throw the trussed and smothering victim into the river. Well, it would be a short and speedy end. St. Margaret had been beheaded, so had St. Catherine. They would pray for her and help her face the executioners with something of their own saintly valour.

This was as good a time as any to prepare for death;

since she was not allowed confession or Holy Communion, since she was cut off from those who could give her spiritual aid and comfort, she had to do as best she could. Her mother had often told Jeanne and her brothers and sisters, when they were children, that no one knew when death might come and that it was wise to be always ready. Jeanne had tried to live in that manner; the only time she had ever endangered her soul was when she leaped from the tower. Her mother had also taught them that in time of great danger, one commended soul and body to the Creator and Father, calling on the aid of the Blessed Mother of God, holy St. Joseph, St. Michael and his angels, St. John the Baptist, St. Peter, St. Paul and all the saints. With sincere fervour one sorrowed for all one's offences against God, with great faith and trust offering Him the bleeding wounds of His beloved Son, through Whose Passion and Death men were saved. And after these things had been done, one kept calm, waited—and trusted.

Slowly she went through her devotions. When they were finished, she felt calmer, noticed that the moon was almost full, wondered where La Hire, Alençon and the rest were fighting and, finally, fell asleep.

She dreamt of Domrémy. . . . Seven years rolled back and she sat, a child of twelve, in the group seated round her parents' hearth. She and her mother and sister teased wool—neither lack of daylight nor presence of company being an excuse for Isabel d'Arc or her daughters to sit with folded hands. The boys and Jacques likewise had occupations that kept their hands occupied while their minds were free to attend to the conversation. Jacquemin helped his father to weave panniers, peeling and whit-

tling the sally saplings that were so pliant in Jacques'
strong fingers. Pierre prepared and supplied waxed ends,
pieces of soaked hide, strings of various thicknesses,
catgut, awls, bodkins and needles, ready-threaded, to
Little-Jean, who was repairing reins and fishing tackle.

It was the night that the two Domrémy pilgrims came
to tell of the great Roman Pilgrimage of 1424; Thévenin
the wheelwright, and Thiesselin the *greffier*, who did
the reading and writing for the people of Domrémy and
Greux, had just returned from doing the Jubilee proclaimed by Pope Martin V. Their first visit, after long
hours of much-needed sleep, had been to Isabel d'Arc;
which was only courteous and fitting, she being the one
who had given them advice and directions before they
set out on their long and perilous journey. Not for nothing was Isabel known locally as Romée; few women in
Lorraine, or indeed in all France, could claim to have
walked to Rome and back, as she had done for the Great
Pardon of 1400. To this inveterate pilgrim others bound
for holy places were wont to come, making enquiries
about road and river routes, about hospices and monasteries where one could be sure of a night's lodging. They
conferred with her about the many hazards of the
way—the brigands who infested the mountain defiles and
lonely moors; the sweltering heat of the south countries;
the sudden and terrible storms; the difficulties encountered when the little collection the neighbours had
made up for the parishioners who volunteered to represent them at the Jubilee dwindled and vanished. They
asked Isabel d'Arc how one managed when hungry; what
one did in Rome; she could be counted upon to have

some preventative for that trial which beset so many pilgrims—sore and bleeding feet.

"Isabel," the Thévenin of Jeanne's dream was speaking, "you were a brave one to set out alone on that journey twenty-four years ago. It nearly killed us, Jacques! How a girl could do it, I cannot say. How did you manage for money? Thiesselin here and I had spent every *gros* the neighbours gave us—even the gold piece the Demoiselle gave us to visit the tombs of the Apostles for her soul's good—all was gone before we were into Lombardy."

"No, you forget," interposed his friend, "we had a little left then; enough, we thought, to take us as far as the Abbey of Vezzolano in Asti; but we had to have our money changed into the coin of that country, and the Jew who changed it fooled us properly—we had barely what bought our food for that day. But how did *you* manage, Isabel?"

"It was different with us. I fell in with a company travelling from Rheims. They gave the Miracles and Mysteries all along the way. In every town we came to, they played in the market-place. They were a clever troupe, picking plays to suit the different audiences. When we neared country rumoured to be ridden with bandits, they played *The Good Samaritan;* in towns where people wealthy—but mean—came to see the plays, they gave *Dives and Lazarus;* always on Fridays they did the *Passion Play* and the *Compassion of Our Lady*. They were good players. People wept when they saw them act *The Prodigal Son*—that was always a great play for loosening purses."

"Did you take part, Mother?" asked one of the boys.

"Only sometimes. I made one of the crowd going to Calvary; I used to try to get among the Daughters of Jerusalem and keep clear of the mob who were shouting 'Crucify Him! Crucify Him!' At the *Marriage of Cana*, I waited at the table. With other plays, I helped the players and mummers dress and mask themselves, and I collected from the crowd; just went round with my pewter pannikin begging 'A penny for the poor palmers! Spare something for the pilgrims! We'll pray for you in Rome, good people, and for the souls of your dead.' That was how the Rheims players went to Rome. I was lucky to have met them."

"I wouldn't doubt my thrifty wife, to get there and back for nothing," remarked Jacques d'Arc, grinning.

"Sure enough, it cost you nothing," said Thévenin, admiration in his voice.

"It cost courage, didn't it, Mother?" asked Jeanne.

"I suppose it did. I was young then and everything comes easy to youth. But it's no easy task to walk to Rome and back."

"We can bear you out in that," averred Thiesselin.

"But it was worth it all to see the Pope and hear him absolve us from our sins," went on Isabel, remembering again the greatest moment of the greatest pilgrimage she had ever done. "Even though there was a rival Pope, we all knew that the Pope in Rome was the rightful one. He was Christ's man in our eyes."

"Thank God the days of the great Schism are over," observed Thévenin. "It was dreadful to have two claiming to be Pope. Please God, we'll never see such dark days again; what matter about the Mussulmen coming from the Bosporus or the Moors up through Spain;

once Christendom is united, the Rock of Peter will stand."

"There are new heresies springing up every other year, the Curé said last Sunday; Lollards in London, and a sect started by some fellow with a queer name—Huss—that's it, in Bohemia. Christian nations would want to stand steady and keep together." Jacques d'Arc sagely nodded his head.

"You'd think, to hear you," said Madame d'Arc, "that you had never heard of the promise that Christ would always remain with His Church and that no matter what evils Hell loosed against us, in the end it's always Christianity that will prevail. But it is a fine thing to have one Pope again, a true Pope, a Pope in Rome."

At a signal from their mother, Jeanne and Catherine rose and began to prepare the supper: *potage*, rye-bread and cheese for Isabel and the younger members of the family; wine for Jacques and the guests, and—as a special gesture to honour the occasion—some of the gingerbread the travellers had brought from Besançon.

While the meal was being prepared, the travellers told the epic tale of their journeyings; of their reception at the great monasteries of Luxeuil, Clairvaux, Hautecombe, and la Grande Chartreuse, each a two-day journey from the other. They told of their trepidation when they turned east from la Grande Chartreuse, making for the Maurienne, the twenty-five league mountain corridor that finally brought them to Mount Cenis—the pass that took one into Piedmont. It was an unnerving experience trudging along that desolate, seemingly-endless valley de l'Arc. No offence to good Jacques and his family, but that valley which bore a name similar to theirs was a sinister one; one seldom saw the sun, so sheer rose the dark crags on either side; the trees grew out sideways giving the place an unnatural appearance; many's the good man had been set upon on that dismal stretch of road; there the robber and the murderer could commit crime after crime with impunity; there the cries of victims went unheard, their bodies unburied. Ah, yes, the tired travellers had not dared to slow pace until they reached the pilgrim hospice on Mount Cenis, where they rested for three days before facing the new perils awaiting them in the foreign lands of Lombardy and Tuscany. They were hospitably received at many fine Abbeys in Italy; especially in the one at Asti and the Columban one at Bobbio. The road south was pleasant going; splendid towns with names that chimed on the tongue like church-bells—Lucca and Volterra; Siena and Grosseto; and, at the end of the road, Rome itself.

The reminiscences continued during the repast, the two neighbours telling their adventures, Isabel recalling some of her own. Finally, there was silence, each one looking into the heart of the fire, busy with his or her own thoughts.

"Mother," asked Jeanne, suddenly, "why does not our Dauphin go to Pope Martin, now that we have a rightful Pope, and get himself proclaimed King of France before all Christendom?"

"Hark at the maid," laughed Jacques, half-apologetically, "always fretting about that Dauphin of ours. I'll warrant he hasn't a more faithful subject in all France. Don't you worry, girl, the Dauphin is well able to look after his own rights."

"But he *should* go to the Pope, shouldn't he? Isn't

France the oldest daughter of the Church? Why doesn't he go?"

Her brothers began to mock at what seemed to them a futile query.

"Why, indeed!" said Madame d'Arc. "I think Jeanne is right. I don't know nor understand the ways and doings of high and mighty folk like kings and dauphins, but if I had a just cause and no means of setting it right, I know where I'd go. I'd walk all that road to Rome again—alone, if I could get no one to accompany me—and I'd tell my story to the Vicar of Christ."

"I believe you would, too," said her husband.

"What's more, I'd abide by his decision. For the Pope is not left alone; he is Christ's man in a way no one else is. Christ Our Lord knows that His Popes are but men like other men, so He stays close to them, very close. And when the children of the Church go with their plaints and woes, they go not to speak into the ear of any other but Christ and, in the Pope's reply, they hear Christ's voice."

"Didn't I tell you," said Jacques, winking at his friends, "that my Isabel knows nearly as much as the Curé? Where she got it all I don't know, but it was a pity she was born a girl—there was a thundering good preacher lost in her."

"I get excited about these things," Isabel apologised, "and my tongue goes a-racing."

The visitors stood up to go; they had little gifts for everyone; a relic of St. Apollonia for Little-Jean, who often suffered from the toothache; one of St. Christopher, patron of travellers, for Isabel, against her next pilgrimage; relics of St. Barbara for Jeanne—St. Barbara was to be invoked against enemies, they said. Jacques and the boys strolled a little way down the village with the departing guests. The girls helped their mother to clear away after the meal, to bank down the fire and tidy the wool, the sally-baskets and the fishing-gear.

"Did you really mean, Mother, that you would go to the Pope if you knew you had a just cause and no hope of getting a fair judgment?" asked Jeanne.

"If I were an old woman of sixty and more, I'd hobble along somehow," replied the mother. "And what's more, every Christian man and woman—aye, and child, too—has the right to go. If the law of the realm, or even ecclesiastical courts in any kingdom, do not give a body a fair hearing, every child of the Church has the right to ask to have his cause heard in Rome. The Pope has the last say in the matter. And, if ever you hear otherwise, don't believe it; tell whatever poor wretch is being unjustly dealt with to go to Rome. But, of course, you will never be in a position where you should advise someone like that. Still, it's well to know these things; one never knows what may happen these bad times. I know that if I saw Christian people unjustly condemned—and by biased judges—I should urge them: 'Ask to be sent to Rome. Say that you wish to be tried by Christ's Vicar and no one else.'" . . .

It was then Jeanne started from her dream, her mother's voice still ringing in her ears—"Ask to be sent to Rome. Say that you wish to be tried by Christ's Vicar and no one else."

.   .   .   .   .

In the morning she was not left long to wonder what was to happen. A wagon awaited her at the prison gate, she was told; a woman's dress was left for her should she wish to wear it; there was water for washing. She washed, but did not don the dress, and announced that she was ready. When they unfastened her chains, she found great difficulty in walking, so long a time had she been without exercise or free movement. But she had not far to walk—from the cell to the wagon, from the wagon to a platform that could never have been erected in so short a time only for the moonlight of the previous night. On a larger platform, Cauchon, the English lords, and members of the tribunal were seated; on the platform ascended by Jeanne and Massieu, an official was waiting, surrounded by scribes and notaries. This official preached a long sermon, during which Jeanne's attention wandered many times. It was so good to be in the open air again. Rouen was a fine city—ships at the quays; spires of many churches; the cemetery nearby had some fine stone crosses and dark yew trees. When her eyes rested on objects nearer at hand, however, there was cause for foreboding. That red-garbed fellow standing by the cart must be Thirache, the famous executioner of Rouen. Why was he here? In his official clothes, too. A little way from him was a stake; its purpose unmistakable, with its chains and its huge pile of faggots and boys with lighted torches standing by. Why was all in readiness? Would that stake be, this evening, like the stakes she had passed on the road to Gien in 1429—a ghastly stump, blackened and smouldering, its chains holding charred embers—the remains of Jeanne d'Arc?

These sombre thoughts made her pay but little heed to

the sermon and exhortation, or to the long list of her errors and of her crimes of witchcraft, heresy and divers other abominations. She pulled herself together when she heard herself called upon by name. Someone was bidding her to submit to the Church for the sake of her immortal soul.

"But I *have* asked all you prelates and doctors of Law that an account of my words and deeds be sent to Rome" . . . ("Speak up boldly," her Voices commanded at that very moment, "answer without fear."). . . . "I refer all to God and to Our Holy Father the Pope." She remembered her vivid dream of the previous night. "Send me to the Pope!" she cried. "I want to be tried by the Pope in Rome."

"The Pope is too far away. These Bishops, especially Pierre Cauchon, the Ordinary of the diocese in which you were captured, are your judges."

This time she made no reply. If her Voices wished her to say more, they would tell her. The Bishop of Beauvais rose and began to read the sentence. Suddenly all was confusion; judges and clerics left their places and surrounded her platform.

"Abjure! Abjure, Jeanne!" they pleaded. What did it mean to "abjure"? It was a new word to her.

"Submit to the Church," others cried, "submit or burn."

She understood what it meant to submit to the Church. She had, she hoped, always done so—not for fear of burning or for any worldly gain, but because the Church was for her that body of which Christ Our Lord was Head, and she, however unworthy, a member. The shouting became a din in which no words could be distinguished. At any time she found it hard to understand the dialect of these Normans; the University professors might be speaking a different language almost, so unlike the *patois* of her native valley was the stately French and unintelligible legal words they used. In this clamour it was hard to know what was required of her. She decided to reply to the one query she had understood.

"I *do* submit to the Church," she said, and was about to repeat her request to be sent to the Pope, when cheers, yells and hisses filled the air. With great haste the official who had preached the sermon and read the list of her misdeeds produced a document which he began to read through quickly, glancing now and again at the prisoner to see if she were attending. She tried to attend, but there was the greatest confusion all about; Cauchon and English prelates were shouting angrily at one another; stones were being flung by the crowd, and the soldiers—spoiling for a fight—were threatening now the Rouennais, now the judges and prelates, now the wretched witch who was the cause of their being kept standing about since early morning.

When she managed to concentrate on what most nearly concerned herself, she found that she was being asked to sign a written paper—not much writing, something about the length of a *Pater Noster*—it was probably a declaration that she submitted to the Holy Catholic Church. Someone was speaking—so many crowded round her that she could not say who it was—promising that if she signed and wore woman's dress, she would be taken to the Church prison. "Holy Archangel Michael, defend us in battle that we may not perish in the tremendous judgment," she prayed; then, taking the pen, she put a cross on the paper. And she smiled as the tumult rose about her, fiercer than ever. She knew that her enemies were well aware that such a sign, coming from her hand, meant denial—and the paper was worthless to them. But, in a moment, an English secretary produced another paper for her signature; he even grabbed at her hand and made as if to guide it; but she scrawled a great O, so that the result of all persuasions and threats was merely two spoiled papers and no signature.

The crowd grew more restive; tension increased; stones were being gathered to throw at her. Some said that it was all trickery; they had been brought to the cemetery of St. Ouen, led to expect a burning, and what sort of entertainment were they getting? Clerics and doctors of Law, English commanders and men-at-arms, all being set at naught by the witch; she had been seen to smile, those nearest the platform said; she was just making mock of her judges.

But Cauchon was not a man to be mocked or set at naught. He had come prepared for this. It suited him well that the English did not take her punishment out of his hands that morning. Execution by the English, with no recantation of her errors by the Maid, would mean that her name would be held in honour by the French. There was to be no honour in this business for either her or her wretched King. He had another document in readiness, which he instructed Massieu to read to the Maid, getting her to recite the words after him. It was not a long document—it contained six lines of large writing—and, with great satisfaction, Cauchon noted that the

Maid was repeating the words, many of which were too difficult for her to comprehend. While she was so engaged, Cauchon slipped another document, signed *Jeanne*, into the sheaf of papers he carried; in this document, in fifty lines of close, minute writing, the Maid accused herself of an appalling list of crimes. Massieu had by this time finished reading to her. "It is enough," said Cauchon, "she has abjured by her own lips."

Jeanne could not quite understand why he said such a thing; the English seemed angry, the crowd divided—some, who pitied her, glad that she had escaped Thirache and the fire; others, who had in their hearts believed in her, grieved that she should have abjured. But had she? She herself hardly knew. She hoped that her days in Warwick's dungeon were over; they had promised to transfer her to the prisons of the Church. But perhaps Cauchon and those others would forget their promise; it might be well to remind them of their pledge. "Churchmen!" she called, "take me to your prisons, that I may be no longer in the hands of these English."

Those in charge of the wagon looked for directions to Cauchon. "Take her back to where you brought her from," ordered the Bishop. So, amid the jeers of the English soldiers, they turned back towards the castle dungeon. "By Heaven!" exploded Warwick, "my young Lord, the King, is ill-served."

"Have no fear," replied Cauchon, his eyes following the cart, "we shall have her yet."

. . . . . .

The wagon began to trundle back to the prison. Jeanne was silent, aghast at the callousness of her enemies. Phrases of the long condemnation still rang in her ears, those last sentences which had just been read aloud to her in the cemetery; the words were easily understood, unlike the learned verbiage which had wearied her hearing and her understanding so much all that day: "Inasmuch as you have rashly sinned against God and the Holy Church, we finally and definitely condemn you for salutary penance to perpetual imprisonment, with the bread of sorrow and water of affliction, that you may weep for your faults and never henceforth commit anything to occasion weeping."

As the wagon-wheels ground discordantly on the cobblestones, they took up the dismal refrain: "Perpetual imprisonment. Perpetual imprisonment." "Penance! Penance! Penance!" screamed the sea-mews, as they circled about the lace-like towers of St. Ouen. "Sorrow. Sorrow. Bread of sorrow," murmured the wood-doves in the trees near the Palais de Justice. "Affliction. Affliction," repeated the tramping boots of the men-at-arms. Was she then, she asked herself, as the cart bore her nearer and nearer the dungeon, to be locked away in this dark, noisome place for life? Would she never again see sun or sky, flower or tree? Would she be cut off forever from the strong current of human life—that ordinary but, to her, suddenly desirable life such as she had glimpsed that morning in her brief passage between the prison and the cemetery—where people like her own good people of Domrémy marketed butter and eggs, garlic and cress and cheeses; where goodwives sat spinning in their door-ways; where girls sang and children laughed and played? Benumbed by the horror of the thought, she suffered herself to be hurried from the cart and up the steps until, finally, she found herself back in her cell. Once there, she lay as one dead, her mind reeling under the impact of her misery, her heart dumbly trying to pray.

Even the entry of five members of the tribunal into her cell sometime during the afternoon did little to rouse her. They spoke of the great mercy God had shown her that day and of how grateful she should be that her judges had received her back into the grace and pardon of the Church; they warned her of what awaited her should she now relapse into her former errors; and they exhorted her to submit humbly to the sentence and ordinances of the tribunal. She had been told that day that she must put off man's clothing and arrange her hair otherwise—she was not to continue wearing it cut like a man's.

"Do you agree to this?" asked one.

"Will you do this, Jeanne?" said another.

"I will be good," she said, wishing that they would leave her. When she opened her eyes again, she was alone in the cell, and a long dress of homespun lay beside her. Wearily, she rose and donned it. In a few minutes, the doctors were back again, bringing with them a barber.

"I could make her a wig," the latter was explaining.

"Which do you desire," asked Midi, "a wig, or——?"

"Cut it all away," she replied.

And so it was done. When the judges and doctors left to report to Cauchon that the prisoner gave evidence of being in proper dispositions, the guards gathered about the cell to mock and laugh at the prisoner, grotesque and jeer-worthy now. For a long while they stood there, calling her names, mocking, telling one another that at last they had a woman prisoner—at least, one formed and dressed like a woman. To be sure, the head put one off; it resembled neither a man's head nor yet a woman's, nor even a new-born child's; it was like a death's head, one fellow remarked lugubriously. At which remark the guards, growing suddenly tired of their game of prisoner-baiting, resumed their dice-play.

But Jeanne had not heard them. There were other Voices speaking to her at that time. St. Catherine had been with her, and St. Margaret. Never before had she realised that they had both been girls of her own age; they, too, had known imprisonment, trial—even torture and death; they, too, were but nineteen. They came to comfort and console. Had they not also known misery such as Jeanne's?

In some strange way the curtain of ten centuries rolled back and Jeanne saw what had happened to Catherine and Margaret. Margaret had suffered in the time of Diocletian. Jeanne saw her, tending the sheep of her foster-parents in the fields near Antioch—fields not un-like those near Domrémy and the Bois Chenu; a lovely maiden, not long baptised into the Christian faith of the family she lived with, Margaret's beauty attracted the Governor, who, riding alone through that remote part of the countryside, discovered with amazement this pearl among women. Yet, when his servants dragged her to his palace, the girl refused not only his advances but even his offer of honourable marriage—unprecedented in the case of an Imperial Governor and a provincial shep-herdess. And for the silly reason that she was a Christian—one of that strange sect who actually worshipped a Galilean malefactor Who had been crucified a few centuries before. Such defiance could not be tolerated. Olibrius, the Governor, decided that a night in prison might make the girl change her mind. In the morning he had her brought before him again; her beauty was astounding—it increased his desire to possess the maiden. Olibrius listened while she answered the judges who questioned her about this Galilean, this Christ—"her Lord," she called Him; He was not dead, she claimed, He still lived—lived eternally. Surely the girl would not persist in such foolishness, surely she would not continue to repulse him, the Governor, if she were threatened with torture.

"Maiden," interrupted Olibrius, "for the sake of your fair body, have pity on yourself. Sacrifice to the gods of our fathers. If you will not abandon these stubborn and foolish beliefs, I will have you torn to pieces."

But the girl had replied: "Jesus suffered death for me. Gladly would I do as much for Him."

Such fine words were easy. When the torture started she would pipe another tune. No maid so fair could endure to have her beauty marred; no one so young and tenderly nurtured could stand torture.

The next day, a broiling July day, when the strong sun beat down upon the market-place, all the people of Antioch came to the trial of Margaret—all, save the Christians, who gathered together in one of their secret meeting-places and prayed without ceasing for the member of Christ about to be put to the torture. The judges bade her sacrifice to the old idols of her ancestors; not much would be asked of her—a throwing of a few grains of incense, a libation of chicken's blood—it would be over and done with in a few moments and Margaret could pass to where a choir of maidens waited to invest her with rich garments befitting her beauty. Then she would be conducted to the white throne placed beside that of Olibrius and all Antioch would rejoice and make holiday.

But the obstinate Christian girl shook her head. She chose, not the choir of maidens, the lovely raiment, the throne set beside the Governor's, but the ranks of torturers, waiting with flaming pine-torches, to close around her in an ever-tightening ring.

The Governor gave the sign; the torture began; but—whether some magic preserved the maid or malice steeled her against crying out—she gave no sign of pain, a phenomenon which greatly awed the multitude. Olibrius, however, seeing a blackened body in place of that which had so attracted him, suddenly felt all desire die in him; in its stead anger raged.

"Behead her," he called to the executioner. The latter was loath to do his task; the condemned one had to encourage him. "My brother," she begged, "take your axe and strike well."

Thus Margaret had entered into Paradise. It had been a little suffering for so infinite a gain, the Saint assured Jeanne.

Catherine had lived at the latter end of the same century the dawn of which Margaret had graced. Of noble birth, she was a scholar of Alexandria, that city of schools and learning. She had dared face Maximin the Thracian to reproach him for torturing her fellow-

Christians; she had gone further and expounded to the tyrant the necessity for believing in Christ. In the beginning Maximin had regarded her as an amusing and novel diversion; it was good sport listening to her refute the pagan philosophers. Later, he thought it would be excellent for his own prestige if he were to score a point over the school men and win Catherine over, not by argument, rather by blandishments and fair promises. But he failed, utterly. Not willing to be defeated in his purpose, he decided to use other and more potent means to make the maiden submit. In her eighteen-year-old body Catherine bore, in turn, the flaying scourge, the leaded whips, the eleven-day deprivation of all food and drink. At the end of this time Catherine was the means of bringing unbearable disgrace and shame upon Maximin. His wife had expressed a wish to see this Christian maid, and Maximin being busy and not particularly desirous of meeting Catherine again, had deputed his first General to escort his wife to the prison. What was his humiliation to discover, a few days later, that Catherine had so seduced her two visitors that they had embraced the Christian faith themselves—making Maximin the laughing-stock of his friends and enemies. That sealed the prisoner's fate.

The knife-studded wheel that was made ready to tear her body asunder having, unaccountably, broken into pieces at the first twist of the handle, Maximin gave the order for her beheading; but the girl went, smiling, to lay her head on the block—those Christians were strange, unpredictable creatures, Maximin told himself, as he returned to the affairs of state. Truly, Catherine told Jeanne, the sufferings of the body bore no relation to those joys entered into when time was changed for eternity; and He Who had promised rewards for the cup of cold water given in His Name and for His sake had wondrous guerdon waiting for all who suffered sooner than deny Him.

And then, gently, the Voices reproached her for having agreed—however slightly—at St. Ouen. Now one, now the other of the two Saints spoke. A few days later, when interrogated on the matter, Jeanne could remember their every word:

"They told me," she said on the following Monday, when Cauchon, accompanied by several assessors and the notaries, hastened to her cell to see for themselves had she relapsed, word having reached the tribunal that she had resumed man's clothing, "my Voices, which I have heard since Thursday, told me that God had pitied me for the treason to which I consented in St. Ouen; they told me that in saving my life I was damning myself. . . . If I were to say that God had not sent me, I should be damning myself, for it is true that God did send me. My Voices have told me, since Thursday, that I did very wrong in doing that which I did, and that I must confess that I did wrong. What I declared on Thursday was done through fear of the fire. Whatever I was made to deny at St. Ouen, I never did anything against God or the Faith; I did not understand what was in the formula of abjuration."

And the notary, Boisguillaume, looking at the silent Cauchon and the others, none of whom betrayed by word or sign what went on within his mind, wrote in the margin of the manuscript whereon he recorded the proceedings: *Responsio Mortifera*—Fatal Reply.

Chapter Fourteen

MAY 30TH was a busy morning in the old Fish Market. The red-uniformed Thirache shouted orders at his two helpers, who were trying to steady the tall stake in the scarcely-set mortar. At the other side of the market, the Master-Carpenter bullied and harangued his guildsmen and handymen. Time was short, and there were three platforms to be erected and adorned, three stands on which Authority would soon sit and see Justice done. The Bailiff of Rouen was there, watching the preparations; he was pleased with the bales of velvet and tapestry that had been ordered by Warwick; he fingered the rich materials, his thrifty mind regretting that they were not being put to better use than the draping of the main dais. He would have to warn those carpenters to be careful where they used nails; it would be a pity if such fine fabrics were torn. Warwick would hardly notice if he appropriated them after the burning; they would come in useful to festoon the balcony of his—the Bailiff's—

house for the morrow's procession; and, after that, if Warwick did no enquiring after them, the tapestries would make nice hangings for his bedchamber, the velvets some elegant doublets and tunics—if his wife did not insist on having them all for her own gowns.

He moved towards Thirache. The executioner was in a very bad humour; those worthless fellows, his assistants, had spent a whole day in the woods, but so meagre and so unsuitable had been the load they brought back that he himself had had to go out during the night—the moon was just on the wane, too, which meant that fever, quinsy and other ailments floated on the night air—and fetch proper faggots, and plenty of them! He did not tell the Bailiff that his all-night wanderings in the nearby forest had taken him much further than half-way to Louviers. He had been hoping to run into some friends of the Maid, some of the captains of the French army. After all, executioners were not so highly paid and had to look out for themselves. Usually, friends of the condemned were on the watch for Thirache, with a good fat bribe if he promised to knock the victim unconscious —'twas easily done with a tap of the hammer when hammering the chains into position, or by throttling with a pull of the chain, or with his bare hands. Thirache considered that he had demeaned his office and himself by riding about all night within reach of the Maid's friends; it was their business to seek *him* out. Worst of all, he had not met them. This Jeanne d'Arc had a poor lot of friends; it was proof positive that she really was as bad as the judges said she was, the way her friends—King, captains, parents and all—had abandoned her. He had

heard rumours of Captain La Hire making attempts to
rescue her. Well, the Captain should have been in the
forest last night waiting for Thirache. That was the best
way to effect a rescue.

Thirache cursed himself for a fool as—feeling the loss
of his night's sleep—he saw to the preparations. By God,
this witch would suffer for the failure of her friends to
pay him his usual bribe; she'd pay for the way he had
ridden his mule round that damned forest all night! He'd
set that stake higher than ever stake was set in Rouen;
she'd burn like a wick atop a long candle, slowly and
painfully. That would teach her friends how they should
have dealt with Thirache. . . .

In the dark cell Jeanne the Maid woke weary and
listless to a new day. She remembered that this was the
eve of the *Fête Dieu*. The gaolers had been talking of the
great Corpus Christi procession; of the altars and arches
being set up (that would be the hammering in the distance); of the arbours and bowers, of the flower-
bedecked houses and clean-swept streets, of the flags and
banners and boughs of cherry and May-blossom that
made lovely the streets where Our Lord was to pass. One
had spoken of his child who, with other children of
Rouen, was making her First Communion on the feast.
. . . Happy burghers of Rouen. Happy children. Free
to hear Mass, to receive Holy Communion, to walk with
Our Lord when He passed by their doors. At the very
beginning of the trial she had been told that, as one
suspected of witchcraft, heresy and other abominable
deeds, she might not receive the sacraments. The hundred and fourteen days of the trial, the months of misery,

the treatment she had suffered at the hands of the gaolers, were as nothing compared to the great hunger she felt— and felt today more than ever—for the Bread of Life.

Since the morning in St. Ouen cemetery, she had often recalled how refreshingly the wind blew and how beautiful were the trees and the green grass, the sky where birds flew free, the brown earth in fields beyond the town where farmers tended crops lately sown. One did not realise what great and grand gifts God gave, until deprived of them. When would she see the blue of the sky and the green of growing things again? Yesterday no one had visited her, but she had heard the gaolers say that the tribunal had met. It was strange that she had not been sent for; not that she wished to attend any more— she was weary of the eternal questionings, unable any longer to keep always on the alert. During the previous days she had incurred the grave displeasure of Cauchon and some learned men who had visited her cell. They upbraided her for having resumed man's clothing. When she explained that the guards had taken away the woman's dress that she had worn since the day at St. Ouen's and left her nothing but her old suit to wear, they had pretended not to hear her and said that she was obstinate in her disobedience. When they had gone, Massieu remained; he was not a good man, even the gaolers knew of his most unclerical philanderings in the town and of the many times he had been reproved by his ecclesiastical superiors for such aberrations; but he was kind and had done what he could, when occasion offered, to make Jeanne's lot more bearable.

"They thought," he began, jerking his head towards

the stairway, from which the footsteps of the departing Cauchon, Warwick and others could still be heard, "that when you wore the woman's gown and had your head shaved, you would have continued to do so. I am afraid it will go ill with you now; they will misconstrue your action in resuming man's clothing as proof that you are unrepentant."

"They broke their promise to me. They said I should go back to Church prison—and that would mean that I might receive the sacraments and hear Mass—but they did not keep their word."

"Why did you resume these, Jeanne?" He indicated the doublet, leggings and short mantle she wore. "You were weeping when we entered."

"It was because of the guards. Several times since Thursday they have attacked me. Two nights ago—the night of Trinity Sunday—they made bets with one another as to which of them would take the greater part of my dress; they came in turns; they tore it from me. For the rest of the night I had to lie awake, fastening the bed-coverings about me as securely as I could."

"But the man's clothing?"

"In the morning I needed to rise; I asked them to fetch me a dress and loose my chains, but they would only give me my old page-suit. I told them that I was forbidden to wear it; they mocked and said nothing would give them greater pleasure than that I go yonder" (she indicated the dark passage to the prison latrines) "in such garments as their sport of the previous night had left me. I waited till almost noon, hoping that they would change their minds or that the Duchess of Bedford might come to visit me; then I could wait no longer—so I took the suit. I had to wear it."

That was two days ago. Neither Massieu nor the judges had come yesterday. This morning there was no one—as yet. She had heard the Matin-bells in the convents of Rouen and wondered how the holy Abbess, Colette, and her good nuns were faring. She hoped they prayed for her. Strange how seldom now her thoughts turned to Domrémy; she might never have had parents, she told herself, so seldom did she think about them of late. She wondered whether she loved them at all. God was her father and mother; Our Lady her dear one; for brothers and sisters she had angels and saints; and all France was her kin.

Footsteps sounded on the stone stairs. Bolts were drawn, keys turned in the triple lock. It was a Dominican father who had been kind to her during the trial; indeed he had got into trouble with Cauchon and Warwick for advising her to appeal to the Church Council meeting at Basle. This morning he looked distressed and pale, did Martin Ladvenu; he did not relish the task entrusted to him; he wasted no time, but blurted out his news. In two hours she was to die—to die by burning. Such was the verdict of the tribunal, and he, unhappy man, had been charged with telling her what awaited her. He was also to help her prepare for death.

So this was what the Voices had meant when they had repeated so often during the past days: "Take things peaceably. Heed not thy martyrdom. Thus shalt thou enter Paradise." Ah, but fire—death by burning! St. Margaret and St. Catherine had known no worse than the swift cut of the sword, coming from behind. St. Michael knew not our mortal death, nor any of the pains of the body. She had seen the charred stake on the road near Gien. Terror gripped her at the memory. Human nature rebelled. She wept and cried aloud: "Must I be so cruelly treated and must my body, that I have always kept pure and incorrupt, be consumed and reduced to ashes? I would rather be beheaded seven times than be burned thus!" Ladvenu waited; he knew the Maid better than she knew herself; this first reaction would subside. He waited and prayed.

In a little while, nature having made its protest, grace prevailed. A Mass-bell was ringing in a nearby church. Nearly always she had heard her Voices when church-bells rang. This time they only said: "Daughter of God. Daughter of God." It was enough to make her realise that within two hours she would enter her Father's House; and there was not much time to make ready for appearing before so great a King, to go home to so dear a Father. But they would not let her receive the sacra-ments. Not now. They had refused her when they re-garded her as a suspect; they would not grant her such a request now that they had decided that she really was guilty of all the dreadful charges they had brought against her. She could hardly believe her ears when Lad-venu told her that, anticipating her request to receive Holy Communion, he had asked for, and obtained, per-mission to administer the sacraments. He did not add that he himself thought it passing strange that the tribunal granted this concession to one they had condemned as a heretic, a witch, an apostate.

She knelt and confessed her sins, all the sins of her

nineteen years. She especially grieved for jumping from the tower at Beaurevoir; it was the only time in her life when she, as far as she could recall, had done something that gravely offended God. She was sorry for all her sins of thought, word, deed and omission; those which she knew, those which she did not know; those which she forgot, those which she remembered; those which had given offence and scandal to others; those that had displeased none but God. And she prayed the Almighty and merciful Lord to forgive her, absolve her and grant her remission of her sins for the sake of Christ Our Lord. The priest gave her a few words of advice as to how she should pray in those last moments when her pain would become almost too much for her to bear. He told her the beautiful story of St. Felicitas, the slave girl who, moaning in the pains of child-birth, was mocked by the Roman guards. They had refused to allow the other women prisoners to come to her assistance. "Christian slave!" they taunted her, "how wilt thou endure being thrown to the beasts, if thou cannot bear these pains, common to all women?" But Felicitas had made answer: "Now it is I who suffer, but then Another will be within me, Who will suffer on my behalf, seeing that it is for Him that I am to suffer." And she bore the martyrdom of being tossed on the horns of wild cattle—she and her mistress, the young Roman matron Perpetua—before being finally dispatched by the sword. Having thus calmed and consoled the Maid, the Dominican gave her absolution and told her to prepare to receive Holy Communion while he arranged to have the Blessed Sacrament brought to her cell.

Not since she had been at Crotoy castle, a stopping

place on the way to Rouen, had she received her Lord. The Chancellor of Amiens Cathedral had been a fellow-prisoner of hers there; he had heard her confession, and she was present each morning at his Mass, and communicated.

Her prayers were interrupted by Ladvenu, who was scolding those bearing the Blessed Sacrament up the steps to the cell. He seemed to be greatly incensed. "Who is responsible for this?" he cried. "Retrace your steps at once! Come in procession; don surplice and stole; bear lights and sound a bell," he ordered. So it was done.

As the little procession came into the condemned girl's cell, litanies were intoned and all present sang "Pray for her! Pray for her!" She received her last Holy Communion with great devotion and many tears. All withdrew while she prostrated herself before the Divine Guest in her soul. Ladvenu walked up and down, passing his rosary through his fingers; he hoped that others were praying for her, too; but in case she were forgotten by all, he redoubled his own fervour and prayed as he never prayed before—as he hoped some one might pray for him in his last hour.

But her prayers had to be brief. They clad her in a long white robe; thrust on her shaven head the hood of infamy, making sure that its wording was visible to all: *Heretic, Relapsed, Apostate, Idolater;* and hustled her into the rough cart that waited to bring her to the market-place. Six score men-at-arms were waiting, armed with sticks, swords and axes, and when she was secured in the cart, they lined up to escort the Maid to her burning.

Down-hill towards the river they marched, through streets packed with people. No man lifted a hand in her defence; not one said a word of comfort. Where were the knights who, not so long agone, had been proud to ride by her side? Fighting a guerilla warfare, now here, now there; never coming within striking distance of Rouen; not effecting a rescue; not sending a word of cheer or remembrance. Where was her father, Jacques d'Arc, the man who had hastened to Rheims the previous July? Her brother Pierre was probably still in prison, but where was her brother Jean, knighted by the King of France for sake of his sister? Where were the friends from Domrémy and Orleans? Where was the King? These were the questions the eight hundred Englishmen—picked men-at-arms and squires who mingled with and controlled the crowds—asked one another. These foreigners were curious to see what she looked like, this warrior-Maid who had inflicted such crushing defeats on their arms, this witch from Lorraine who had been found guilty of sorcery, blasphemy and other heinous crimes. They expected a bold-faced hoyden, swaggering and foul-mouthed, a depraved creature against whose evil eye God-fearing Christians crossed themselves and prayed. They saw, instead, a tall, quiet girl whose face bore traces of tears, whose lips trembled; her eyes were kind, her bearing gracious and womanly; her low voice reached the crowd that pressed upon her from all sides— she was asking for prayers. Witches did not ask for prayers, people told one another. It was sad to see so fine a girl—and one so young—being brought to the stake.

At the foot of the hill, the wagon, with its escort of

archers, turned sharply to the right and entered the Old Fish Market, cleared of its fish-women, its onion and apple-sellers, its cider booths and its stalls, where Jew pedlars sold trinkets and gadgets, amulets and relics. All these people were gathered—together with their goods and their gear—at one corner of the square, grumbling at the high-handed manner in which their business had been impeded, on a day that had promised to be good for selling—the eve of the *Fête Dieu*.

Jeanne braced herself for what lay ahead. When she concentrated on her prayers, she managed to keep her rising terror under control; but when she allowed her attention to stray towards those about her, the realisation of her position almost overwhelmed her. At one street corner stood Pierre Cusquel, the workman who had so often chatted with her in her cell. His wife and himself were in the front line of onlookers. He lifted his hand in salute when the wagon came near enough for its occupant to recognise him. He could not speak; sobs choked him; after all, the girl was but the same age as his own daughters; it was a hard end for one so young, he told those about him, but he was careful to speak in a whisper; already the English had turned on one of the judges who had run from out the crowd to beg the Maid's pardon as she passed. Warwick had ridden up and ordered the conscience-smitten Doctor to take himself away from Rouen as speedily as possible, otherwise he might find himself in grave danger from the soldiers.

On a balcony, surrounded by her ladies, stood the Duchess of Bedford. Not many years older than the prisoner, Anne of Burgundy was filled with compassion for the Maid now doomed to so horrible a death. It was sad to die so young, she told her ladies, little thinking that before many moons passed by, she herself would have gone the way of all flesh. Glancing towards the balcony and beholding her benefactress in tears, Jeanne broke down completely; her sobs and lamentations for the rest of the way caused even the soldiers in the crowd to feel pity for her. But the Voices reminded her of her own war-cry—one that had never failed to rally her forces at Orleans. "Courage!" they said, "Courage! Heed not your martyrdom. Through it you enter Paradise." And, by degrees, she regained control of herself.

During the long preliminaries, she listened with patience and calmness. The days of battle were over. Peace was at hand. But the soldiers fumed impatiently. It was past their dinner-hour. "Have an end of this," they shouted. "Will it be St. Ouen all over again? Are we to remain here all day?" And the street-sellers, anxious to resume their trading now that such crowds were about the market, took up the cry of the men-at-arms and archers. So the Bailiff of Rouen waved his hand and said, "Away with her."

Quickly she was seized, hoisted on to the scaffold, thrust into the centre of the great pile of faggots. Thirache spat on his hands before taking the chains to make them fast about her body; this was the one who had none to pay a single gold piece for her, that her sufferings might be lessened. Well, Thirache was being paid by the English for this execution and he would see they got value for their money.

Ladvenu noticed that the Maid was asking for something and clambered up to hear; she asked for a cross, so he ran to fetch the great processional crucifix from the nearby church of St. Sauveur. The girl's eyes following him noticed that she was facing the open door of the church; she would keep her eyes and thoughts there and try to remember the Saviour on His Cross. If only the mad hammering of her heart and the throbbing pulse in her throat would ease down! Cold sweat ran down her face and in the hollow between her shoulder-blades where the chains, criss-crossed upon her bosom and forearms, pulled her back erect against the stake. In every crisis God's grace had come to strengthen her weakness. It did not fail her now. As Ladvenu hurried back, he saw that the executioner had set the fire alight from below; the Dominican, his black and white robes flying behind him, scrambled up the heap of rubble and mortar, holding the Sign of Salvation before the eyes already smarting and streaming from the smoke that swirled upwards. "Go down," she begged, "go down; lest you also burn." He was the last to have speech with her. . . . After that she spoke only to Heaven. . . .

The fire began its grim work. Skin scorched and blistered and shrivelled; heat seared deeper and deeper, searching the sinews, probing through bones, penetrating even to the marrow; flame laved the tortured limbs whose every nerve agonised. Thirache was suddenly in a hurry to be done. He had made no money out of the Maid's friends. He had given her as hard an end as ever criminal got; his work was as good as done, and an evening in a wine-shop was what he needed most after his night in the forest, he told himself. He threw sulphur and tallow on the faggots. The fire roared and sheets of flame hid the stake and its burden. It came as a shock to him when the last words of the Maid rang through the smoke, for they were not words that one would expect a witch to use in her agony. They were the words all good Christians—and, indeed, many Christians leading ungodly lives—hoped to have on their own lips at the hour of death. "*Jesu!*" she cried; and again, "*Jesu! Jesu!*"

The executioner tossed the last few bundles of faggots on to the fire. They had been seasoned and dry, those faggots he had gathered last night in the forest. Yet, despite their noisy crackling and the blaze with which they burned high against the noon-day sun, there was no drowning the piteous cries of "*Jesu!*" that rang from the heart of the flames. In his long experience no one of all those Thirache had burnt at the stake had cried so loudly as did this Lorraine lass that last time she uttered the Name of Our Lord.

His two assistants swept in the remains of the brushwood, while the executioner stood back, carefully flicking the smuts off his red suit—the official clothes he donned only for burnings. It had been quite a while now since that last loud "*Jesu!*" had pierced the clouds of smoke and flame. She should be dead, this one whom the English called *witch* and the French *saint*. It was part of Thirache's duty to show how well he had done his work; waiting a few minutes more for the last twigs and old branches to kindle and burn themselves out, he signed his assistants to fork away the mass of embers, tossing some to the back, some to the sides of the great heap of mortar and rubble. The smoke parted like grey curtains to disclose the poor corpse hanging limply in its chains; the limbs, so straight and finely-formed when Thirache had made fast the bonds, were now contorted and blackened; the head that the Maid had always carried so erect—with the coal-black hair cut to chin level, like a page-boy's—now fell forward, as unsightly as the charred chest and bosom on which it lolled; the chains that bound her still held smouldering remnants of the long robe she had begged to be allowed to wear to her burning.

"Dead!" cried Thirache, pointing to the stake and its burden.

"Dead!" exulted the Maid's enemies. "The witch is dead. The harlot of the Armagnacs could make no spell strong enough to save her from the fire. The devil has got his own at last!"

"The Maid is dead!" The whisper ran through the crowds that packed the Old Market in Rouen, like a rain-laden wind swishing through ripening corn; heads lifted only to droop again. . . . The Maid was dead. . . . Hope was dead.

Slowly, the people began to move away; already the English captains were shouting orders to the eight hundred archers who had escorted the Maid from Warwick's dungeon to the stake. Thirache proceeded with his grim task. He had been warned that there must be no remains of the Maid. Cauchon, Bishop of Beauvais, had warned him. Warwick, the English Commander, had warned him. One said he did not want her partisans venerating her ashes as the relics of a martyr; the other said that witch-remains being in much demand by those who practised sorcery—and they were many—Thirache should see to it that there was nothing for such wicked ones to carry away. Bidding his helpers pile up the remains of the firewood about the butt of the stake, the executioner added the charcoal he had ready, dashing all generously with sulphur and oil. There! The orders of the Earl and the Bishop would be carried out to the letter. What could withstand that heat? The new conflagration burned with such intensity that he had to move down from the mortar-heap; drawing his arm across his brow every now and then to wipe away the sweat, he stood watching the crowd disperse.

On the far side of the Old Market stood John Tressart, Secretary to the King of England. He was a queer one. Thirache had seen him turn away and strike his breast while his countrymen cheered in derision at the dead witch. "We are lost," he kept muttering, "we have burnt a saint!" A group was still listening to that other Englishman, the archer who had crept in near the stake to fulfil a vow he had made some months before; he had vowed to add an extra stick to the fire. It was just then that she had called on Our Lord with that last great cry. The Englishman had clutched at Thirache, one moment yelling that the Holy Name was written in the flames, the next raving about a dove that flew aloft from out the fire. Half-crazed he had seemed; it was unusual for the English *Goddams* to gibber and shake like that; they were a taciturn lot, adept at concealing their feelings. Thirache threw more tallow on the fire and shouted at his men to keep shoving in the embers.

Even the stake was burning fiercely now. Soon his work would be done.

By degrees the crowd ebbed away. The fish-wives, whose business had been held up by the burning, were carrying their baskets and stands to where they usually stood, grumbling loudly over the loss of trade. Their children gathered round Thirache, to watch him at work. Some of them had seen him before, busy at his awful trade. They plied him with questions.

"Did you strangle her with a rope, Thirache, or with your hands?"

"No," answered the executioner. "Not this one."

"Why not, Thirache? Don't you always strangle them first?"

"Only the ones who have friends to pay me well— before and after."

"Had the Maid no friend to pay for her?"

"Not one in Rouen. She had friends a-plenty in Orleans and at Rheims, I hear. The two Dominicans, Ladvenu and Isambard, were the only ones to befriend her today; they have no gold to bribe anyone; not a *sou* between them, let alone a gold piece."

"But, Thirache, were you not sorry for her? She was only as old as your own Marie."

"Out of my way, chattering ones, and let me finish."

Chasing the children away, Thirache turned back to the spent fire and began raking, raking. Christ in Heaven! What was that in the embers? A heart! Her heart—unhurt by the flames and distended with blood. Such a thing had never happened before. In a frenzy he raked all together again, flinging the last of the oil and sulphur on to the glowing charcoal. Where had those worthless helpers of his gone? Into some wine-shop nearby, probably, taking advantage of the few minutes Thirache had spent with the children. He walked up and down waiting for this last fire to burn out, pondering now the burning, now the unburnt heart, now the children's chatter. Memories of Marie, who had died of the plague only recently, came to his mind. What if it were Marie who had been bound to that stake? He had raised it so far aloft above the rough mortar platform that the torments of the Maid must have been worse than those of anyone Thirache had ever burned. . . .

There; the flames had flickered and died. Now, he could surely go and report to hard-faced Warwick and to Pierre Cauchon. But no, it lay as he had left it, that untouched, unscorched heart of flesh and blood. He stared at it, horror-stricken. Slowly his mind struggled with the problem. It was a heart like any other heart. Why then had it remained unconsumed in the terrible heat to which it had been subjected? Why? If she were a witch, her heart would have perished; Thirache had burned witches time and again, and never once had the fire failed to function, drying the blood and burning the flesh and in the end reducing all to ashes. So, Thirache reasoned, the Maid was no witch. But what was she, then? A patriot? Even patriots were not proof against fire; Thirache had burned many a patriot's body; he remembered well, for their friends usually bribed him to strangle or stun them. Slowly, fearfully, Thirache came to the conclusion that the heart of this Maid of Orleans was immune to the flames because it was the heart of one dear to God. He it was Who had said to the fire: "Be cold, burn no more," when it would have laid its tawny fingers on that which He wished to preserve intact. And the fire had obeyed. Was it not as truly His servant as were the winds and the waves?

But it was he, Thirache the executioner, who had with his own hands made a martyr. He had tortured a saint of God. Others he had strangled; even that scant relief he had denied her. It was not to be borne, the torment of mind that surged in upon him. Lest his reason give way under the sudden deluge of misery, he fled from the Old Market to the Dominican Priory, not far away. Isambard and Ladvenu, the two who had befriended the Maid, were walking in the quiet of the garden. "Fathers!" cried Thirache, thrusting his red-garbed self between the black and cream robes of the Dominicans, "I am damned! I have burned a saint. God will never forgive me. He preserved her heart unhurt in the hottest fire I ever made!" And he told them of what had happened.

"Come and see for yourselves, Fathers. Nothing remains but ashes, and her heart—filled with blood. Such a thing was never known. And it was I who burned her; burned one whose heart was so truly God's that He would not suffer it to be destroyed. And I did not raise a finger to ease her sufferings. Others I strangled to save them torture. I let her face the torments I knew were before her. I made no excuse when Warwick—may his name die with him!—gave his orders. 'We'll make an example of her,' he said; 'let the French King and his men see what we think of their *Pucelle*. Build the witch's scaffold high and let her burn long, that all may

see how the English deal with spell-mongers and sor-
cerers. Let them see if her Voices will come to save her.'
And I obeyed him well. I gave her an awful death—God's
holy one. I will never be pardoned. I am damned for
ever!"

"That is no way for a Christian to speak," said Father
Isambard, sternly. "Thus Judas spoke, yet even he would
have been forgiven had he sorrowed for the hurt he did
Our Lord."

"You were but the instrument of others," consoled
Ladvenu. "We will come back with you and see this
wonder."

As Thirache, miserable and worried, was raking the
ashes to show the heart to the Maid's friends, Warwick
and Cauchon arrived to see if their orders had been
carried out.

"What brings you two back here?" Warwick demanded, remembering how Ladvenu had served the
Maid in her last moments, holding up the crucifix until
she had bidden him descend lest the flames envelop him.

"This!" the executioner answered for the friars, pointing to the heart. "I brought them to see the miracle.
With oil and sulphur and three fierce fires I tried to burn
her heart, but, see!—God has preserved it!"

"Devilry and witchcraft have preserved it." Cauchon's
face was livid with rage. "Back to your priory, monks;
I know why you came back here. You hoped to rescue
the witch's heart and place it in a reliquary. Then her
followers would come to pray there and leave rich offerings to the Dominicans. Begone!"

Warwick, unconvinced, sent his squire back to the

keep for grease, sulphur and faggots. As he waited for these combustibles, he stared at the heart of the rebel Maid. In death, as in life, she was a trouble-maker, he told himself. Soon the squire was back, and Warwick himself helped Thirache, suddenly grown inefficient at his work, to kindle and light a hot fire; taking the rake, he himself tossed the heart into the centre of the flames. Then, standing by, they waited. . . .

"Rake out now," ordered Cauchon, as the fire petered out in thinner and thinner wisps of smoke. Indestructible as ever, there lay that which so much offended them—the unshrivelled heart—on its bed of ashes. The Commander strode towards his charger, undid the saddle-blanket, and spread it on the ground near the stake.

"Sweep all into this," he ordered Thirache, "and carry it to the quay. We shall walk behind you."

Thirache would have liked to disobey, but the great English Earl was a hard man. Slowly, the executioner did as he was bidden. "Tomorrow is Corpus Christi, the *Fête Dieu*," Warwick reminded Cauchon. "There will be a procession. There must be nothing here for anyone to see. Now, executioner, go on before us quietly and quickly. We want no crowds gathering about. And, have a care, no stumbling and losing your load in the gutters; though, indeed, among the garbage and stinking fish-heads would be the proper burial-place for the witch's ashes."

It was pitifully light, what Thirache carried to the Seine-side. Behind the remains of the Maid there walked no mourners, only her most exalted enemies. His mind benumbed with woe and remorse, Thirache obeyed mechanically when Warwick and Cauchon demanded the blanket. He watched as they shook it wide of the quay-wall. The ashes blew about in the afternoon breeze before finally settling on the slow waters beneath. Thirache wondered if the heart would float, but, suddenly blinded with tears, he could not see what happened when it plashed softly in the Seine. In a dream, he followed those who were to pay him for his day's work, back to Warwick's castle, his heart grieving for that other heart now moving seawards with the ebb-tide . . . for the Maid leaving France. The others were jubilant. There, they said, was the end of Jeanne d'Arc. Soon the last of her would be lost in the Western Sea—her grave the limitless wastes of water that stretched forever westward, going on without end beyond the remote land of Erin, that island which, as everyone knew, lay on the rim of God's world.

Epilogue

IT WAS a quarter of a century later. Thirache, hobbling
on two sticks, dragged his creaking old bones to
where the crowd had gathered in the centre of the Old
Market. This was to be a wonderful day. A cross would
be erected where once the stake had stood. Learned
judges, some sent by the Pope himself, would read a
proclamation vindicating the Maid and censuring her
accusers. Where were they now, the enemies who had
encompassed her death? Midi, dead of leprosy. D'Estivet's
corpse found on a dung-heap outside a house of ill-fame.
Cauchon—false to friends, country and Church alike—had
died in his bed, but how? Called suddenly from his sleep
to go before his God, unshriven, unhouseled, unaneled.
Where were the English, so arrogant in Rouen that
morning when, at their bidding, Thirache had burned
the Maid? Driven from French soil; getting a taste in
their own island of what civil war was like. Their war
had a fine name—the Wars of the Roses—but war was
always war, no matter what one called it. France had

302

had a Hundred Years War. Good Frenchmen and women prayed that they might now have a Hundred Years Peace.

The people made way for Thirache. Long since, he had changed his trade of executioner for that of care-taker of the Old Market. Day in, day out, he had tended the little square where pilgrims came to pray and where now the cross was being lifted into position. He hobbled along until he stood beside the Maid's mother. How often she had come as a pilgrim to where her daughter had died! How often Thirache had told her the story of the heart!

She stood erect, Isabel d'Arc, as became the mother of the girl who had saved France. The crowd pointed her out to one another. Ah, she was a woman among thousands, the old peasant woman from Domrémy—that obscure hamlet on the marches of Lorraine! She showed the world the mettle of which the mothers of saints are made! Hers was an indomitable spirit. During the victory of Orleans and the coronation at Rheims she had remained quietly at home. But—despite poverty, advancing years, chronic illness and complete lack of influence—the moment news of the Rouen verdict and burning reached Domrémy she had uprooted herself to see justice done to her daughter. At sixty she had gone to live in Orleans, in the house that Jeanne had leased—the house near the church. From that city she sent petition after petition to Rome, begging for a just enquiry into her child's trial and condemnation. Nay, in her late sixties, had she not travelled from Orleans to the Jubilee of 1450 in Rome, laying her daughter's cause before Pope Nicholas. To be sure, she had powerful backing on that occasion; with her were Count Dunois, better known as le Bâtard d'Orléans, and the wealthy Boucher family, and several learned churchmen who had disagreed with the judgment of Bishop Cauchon's tribunal as strongly as they disapproved of Pierre Cauchon himself. But Pope Nicholas was hesitant; he did not wish to antagonise the English; only a few months before that Holy Year, he had founded the University of Glasgow. Besides, relations between himself and Charles VII, the same whom Jeanne had led to his crowning in Rheims, were strained. He heard poor Isabel's plaints, he listened to the opinions and arguments of the learned doctors and theologians, but he did nothing.

In 1455 he died; some said that his death had been hastened by the news of the defeat of the Greeks and their Emperor, Constantine, in the city of Constantinople at the hands of the Ottoman Turks. There were those who muttered that Nicholas, the great lover of Greek literature, grieved more for Greece, the home of Homer and Plato, than for Greece of the Christians, now overrun by the infidel; that he mourned more for the closing of the schools of Constantinople than for the converting of the noble church, erected by Justinian, into a Mosque for the followers of Mahomet. In 1455, Borgia, the Spaniard, succeeded Nicholas, becoming Pope Callixtus III. To him Isabel d'Arc made haste to appeal; her days were drawing to a close; great work had yet to be accomplished before she could go to her rest. She lost no time and she spared no effort. The proof of her tenacity and valour was her success—as witness the crowds of nobles and dignitaries crowded into the Old Fish Market that bright July morning in 1456.

Thirache had heard of the scenes in the Cathedral of Paris when she appeared on the witness-stand, a bent and haggard septuagenarian, weeping bitterly as she recalled her child's wrongs and sufferings. Enormous crowds of the citizens—of a city never partial to the Maid—had filled the Cathedral and its precincts to overflowing; they craned to hear the decrepit old woman who was asking, owing to her age and debility, to be excused from all but the most important sittings of the tribunal. When Isabel d'Arc left the witness box, the excitement and the emotion were such that the judges had to withdraw and defer the sitting, lest the impartiality of the trial be prejudiced from the start. Yes, she was a woman among thousands, old Isabel. Thirache was proud to be her friend.

Beyond Isabel stood many good neighbours from Domrémy and the Maid's youngest brother, Jacquemin, a quiet farmer who had made no history, but lived his years in that gentle countryside by the Meuse, more engrossed with his cattle and crops than with the affairs of which his famous sister was central pivot.

Standing there also were the brother-knights, Pierre and Little-Jean du Lys. Thirache did not think so highly of these two brothers; he had heard too much that was not to their credit. The moment they heard that their sister had been given what almost amounted to command of the King's armies, they had ridden off to join her, graduating to high military rank and, later on, to knighthood on the strength of her victories. Pierre, the one

who was captured the same time as the Maid, was lucky
enough to have left a sweetheart in his native valley—a
faithful girl who used her dowry to ransom him. People
said queer things about these two brothers when, five
years after Jeanne's death, an impostor came on the scene
claiming to be the Maid. Whether she claimed to have
escaped the flames, or to have got someone else to take
her place at the stake, or to be returned from Heaven,
no one knew for certain. But, from her behaviour, both
during and after her impersonation of Jeanne d'Arc, she
showed herself to be nothing more than a brazen ad-
venturess. Yet Pierre and Little-Jean had supported her
strongly. Perhaps they were deceived by this pretender
in the beginning, but it could not have been long before
they discovered their mistake. Why, folks asked one
another, had they continued to publicly acknowledge
the woman as their sister and to warmly espouse her
cause—riding now to the King, now to the city of
Orleans with her "messages from Heaven," demanding
money for her as the saviour of Orleans? Had they been
ashamed to confess their blunder, or had they hoped to
gain further advancement by backing up this mas-
querader? Only that they stood close behind their good
mother this morning, they would have heard little to
puff them up. A saintly sister or a wretched usurper—
'twas all the same to those two d'Arc cockerels, the
crowd said—it only meant for those shrewd fellows a
chance to elevate and exalt themselves, to gather wealth
and honours.

There, too, were the captains and maréchals and great
lords who had fought side by side with the Maid on

Orleans' walls and elsewhere; La Hire and Le Bâtard—
now Count Dunois—and elegant Alençon and the Lavals.
They were all here today for her triumph, Thirache
mused, the July sun making him sleepy . . . None of
them had been there when she most needed them. . . .
Where, oh, where, was the ingrate King, who had spent
on La Trémoille and other favourites many times the
sum needed to ransom the girl to whom he owed his very
kingship? It might be as well for him not to show himself
here this morning. His conduct the previous year, when
he reneged his noble treasurer and benefactor, Jacques
Cœur, seizing that great merchant-prince's almost fabu-
lous wealth and turning him penniless into exile, was not
to Charles' credit. Christian men were glad to hear that
the Pope, Callixtus III, had received the impoverished
exile who had once been foolish enough to tell his king,
"All I have is yours." No, Charles would not show himself here this morning. Though he was now King of all
France, his abandonment of the Maid was remembered!

Ah, no, the poor girl had had none of these fine friends
with her at the last. . . . Only Thirache had been with
her then. . . . And he had failed her. . . . The preacher
was thundering: "*I call upon my God.*" Thirache felt
suddenly consoled. If he had strangled her as he had
strangled so many others she would never have died calling on Our Lord, and no one would have known her
final dispositions. "*And there are some of whom there is
no memorial,*" continued the preacher, "*who are perished
as if they had never been.*" Thirache remembered the
heart. Where was it now? Had He Who preserved it in
the fire, preserved it in the sea? Had it gone, that brave

young heart, to bring its warrior courage and aid to the Irish, that people who had lent so many saints and scholars to France, who were so constantly at grips with France's ancient enemy?

The old man pondered long; he lost the thread of the preacher's discourse; he forgot the crowd and the grand folk and good old Isabel and all. . . . His thoughts, escaping from his control, fled in all directions, then slowly re-assembled themselves into a golden dream. And in that dream, Thirache saw where God had hidden the heart of the Maid of France. It was in the only grave big enough to hold its greatness—the waters of the world. It would be borne hither and thither for all time, bringing now to this country, now to that, something of its own courage and faith and holiness and love.

FINIS

Feast of the Assumption, Holy Year 1950.